THE Health & Safety HANDBOOK

Al Hinde, Charlie Kavanagh

Editor

Jill Barlow

Published by
The Directory of Social Change
24 Stephenson Way
London NW1 2DP
Tel: 0171 209 5151, fax: 0171 209 5049
e-mail: info@d-s-c.demon.co.uk
from whom further copies and a full publications list are available.

The Directory of Social Change is Registered Charity no. 800517

This book is published in association with Community Health Advice & Training (CHAT) Project, supported by the National Lottery Charities Board. CHAT is a subsidiary of Liverpool Occupational Health Project, registered charity no. 1033189 and company limited by guarantee no. 2892625.

First published 1998

ISBN 1 900360 25 x

British Library Cataloguing in Publication Data
A catalogue record for this book is available from the British Library

Cover design by Kate Bass
Designed and typeset by Kate Bass
Printed and bound by Page Bros., Norwich

Directory of Social Change London Office:
Courses and Conferences tel: 0171 209 4949
Charity Fair tel: 0171 209 1015
Research tel: 0171 209 4422
Finance and Administration tel: 0171 209 0902

Directory of Social Change Northern Office:
3rd Floor, Federation House, Hope Street, Liverpool L1 9BW
Courses and Conferences tel: 0151 708 0117
Research tel: 0151 708 0136

ABOUT THE AUTHORS

Al Hinde

Currently works for the Community Health Advice & Training Project (funded by the National Lottery Charities Board) in South Liverpool, offering health and safety advice to voluntary and community groups.

A qualified mechanical engineer, Al has held various positions in health, safety and training with major UK companies and holds a diploma in Health & Safety, awarded by The National Examination Board for Occupational Safety and Health (NEBOSH).

Having been an active member of the Association of Lions Clubs International for 24 years, Al has considerable experience in various community based activities, including welfare and fundraising.

He is currently a District Safety Officer for the Lions Clubs in the counties of Lancashire and Cumbria.

Charlie Kavanagh

Charlie Kavanagh has worked for the Liverpool Occupational Health Project for eight years and manages two of its subsidiary projects – the Community Health Advice and Training Project (CHAT) and the Safety and Support Project (SAS) which offers help and safety support to small businesses in Liverpool.

He has extensive experience of the voluntary sector, and was the Company Secretary of the Stephen Park trust for four years, which provided a countryside residential centre in rural Lancashire for use by schools and community groups in Merseyside. He has held the post of Honorary Secretary to the Liverpool and District Victims of Asbestos Support Group since its inception in 1993. The group helps individuals affected by asbestos, and their families.

Jill Barlow

Jill Barlow is the manager of Liverpool Occupational Health Project, which is an independent research and development organisation striving to address and prevent health problems due to work. It has done some innovative work in general practices, informing patients about occupational health issues, and facilitating general practice teams, as organisations in their own right, to develop their own action plans to address health and safety. Both Jill and Charlie have written a range of articles on work-related ill health.

She is a member of the National Association of Occupational Health Projects and the National Occupational Health Forum, and is currently working towards an MSc in Health at Liverpool John Moores University.

Contents

How to use this book

This is a practical step-by-step guide to building up your health and safety policy. We advise that you read the book first, and then work through the book, filling in the checklist in appendix 1 and completing the health and safety policy in appendix 2 as you go along. The policy should be as individual as your organisation – it is not something you can get off a shelf.

Don't forget that the policy is not set in stone, and needs to change as your organisation changes.

The book will also act as a source of reference for all your health and safety needs. It covers current health and safety legislation, but you need to be aware that such legislation will change from time to time and you should incorporate any changes in relevant legislation in your policy.

Introduction

Voluntary organisations have a duty to ensure good standards of health and safety for their employees, volunteers, members of their governing body and the public. In writing this book we have attempted to produce a guide on health and safety for the voluntary sector which can be easily read and will meet the needs of all members of the sector, from the small, local group with only a handful of volunteers and an income of a few pounds, to the much larger organisation with many paid employees and an annual income of millions.

This book will help you to deal with health and safety in a simple and practical way. Although managing health and safety issues can be difficult, this book gives you clear guidelines on what to do, how to do it and who to consult. We have attempted to make the process as uncomplicated and as straightforward as possible, and we have used practical examples to clarify legal and technical points made.

We believe the book will have been successful if it helps to improve attitudes towards managing health and safety in the voluntary sector – this should not be treated as a chore which can be completed and then forgotten. There needs to be an ongoing commitment to incorporating good health and safety standards into all your activities.

We strongly recommend that every organisation should attempt to implement all the health and safety requirements of the present law to paid staff and volunteers alike. Even though there are fewer legal obligations for volunteers compared to employees, there is a strong moral case to apply the same health and safety standards to all people involved in an organisation's activities. Organisations which pride themselves on their non-discriminatory practice would find it hard to justify offering different standards of health and safety to volunteers than those offered to paid staff. We also believe that grant-awarding bodies have a moral responsibility to request evidence of satisfactory health and safety procedures, as they do already with equal opportunities policies.

Ultimately, we hope this book will help individual organisations to begin the process of improving their health and safety, thus protecting one of the most valuable assets of the voluntary sector – its people.

HEALTH AND SAFETY IN THE VOLUNTARY SECTOR

Accidents and ill health due to work have a huge human and financial cost in this country – 187 million days are lost every year and the economy loses nearly £12 billion a year as a result. The voluntary sector is playing an ever more important role in society. In the five years up to 1995, the number of organisations grew by 20% and it now has more than 400,000 employees and almost 3 million volunteers. Although 80% of organisations are still relatively small and have incomes of less than £10,000, the sector as a whole has income of more than £12 billion.

Health and safety law has not been written with the voluntary sector in mind. This has led to some areas of health and safety law concerning the sector being under-developed, and the legal responsibility placed on voluntary sector organisations is ill-defined and confusing in some cases. However, we should never forget that health and safety legislation has led to an overwhelming reduction in accidents and illness in this country and is designed to minimise the risk of injury to all people at work.

Much of the good work achieved by the voluntary sector stems from the enthusiasm and commitment of members of governing bodies, employees and volunteers, but good intentions alone are not always sufficient in producing an effective organisation. Good management is crucial. This presents some organisations with a moral dilemma – although it is appreciated that resources need to be managed efficiently, there may be an understandable reluctance to spend time or money on internal management rather than the organisation's main cause or purpose. However this can be a false economy, particularly in the case of health and safety – how can an organisation care for others when they do not care for themselves?

It is vital that the management of health and safety in an organisation receives the same amount of attention as other important issues such as the management of staff, financial controls, and the quality of service or product. Voluntary organisations can ill afford to wait until an accident occurs due to negligence, and they are faced with potential fines and legal action.

Although no separate figures are collected to quantify the accidents or ill health which have occurred in the voluntary sector, given the scale of the problem, the size of the sector and recent high profile cases, it is safe to assume the sector has no room for complacency.

Complying with health and safety law is a positive process which can benefit both the organisation and individuals, paid or unpaid, by improving morale, reducing staff/volunteer turnover and absenteeism. So it is clearly in everyone's interest to have good health and safety procedures and practices in place. Writing out a health and safety policy and carrying out risk assessments will help you to prioritise areas of greatest need and set an action plan in motion for future improvements.

You should adopt this approach for several reasons, not least of which if an accident occurs, the action you have taken to reduce risk will go a long way to show that you are taking health and safety seriously. It will also help to protect your organisation's good name and may limit legal action by showing that you have attempted to comply with your duties to others.

What about your organisation?

If your organisation employs paid staff, it will be treated as a small business by the enforcing authorities and you will have to meet the legal health and safety requirements such as carrying out risk assessments, providing employers' liability insurance and meeting fire regulations. The definition of an employee is an individual working full or part time, doing manual, clerical or any other kind of work, who has a contract of employment. This applies whether the contract is written, or agreed verbally. Note that payment of some expenses may constitute an employment contract, so a clear distinction between employees and volunteers should be made in your organisation.

If your organisation only has volunteers, as a member of the governing body or the person in charge you still have a legal responsibility to them and to members of the public. This responsibility is called duty of care and under law you have a duty to protect volunteers and members of the public from hazards resulting from your organisation's activities.

Most importantly, looking after the health and safety of your staff, volunteers and users is also a practical demonstration of the value you attach to them.

Authors' notes

1. This book has been produced to help those who have responsibility for the health and safety of voluntary and community organisations to comply with their legal responsibilities and/or duty of care.

2. In this book the term 'organisation' is used to include clubs, groups, social organisations, charities, or any other non-profit-making organisation working in the voluntary sector.

3. The trustees of a charity are the people responsible under a charity's governing document for 'the general control and management of the administration of a charity. If your organisation is an unincorporated association, the charity's trustees will be members of the executive or management committee, or if your organisation is a charitable company, the trustees are usually called the board of directors. For ease of reference and clarity, we have used the term 'members of the governing body' for all people with legal responsibility for the administration and management of voluntary organisations in this book.

4. If you are responsible for a voluntary organisation as a member of a governing body, then you and your fellow members have a shared responsibility to understand and control the hazards associated with the organisation's activities – even if the day-to-day responsibility is delegated to an individual, whether paid or unpaid.

5. All organisations, no matter how small or how infrequently they meet or organise events, need to understand the health and safety legal requirements which are relevant to them. Ignorance of the need to comply with health and safety law or duty of care is not a defence in court.

6. Complying with health and safety responsibilities can sometimes be difficult, but by using this book as a guide you can begin to organise and manage your health and safety. It should not be used as a short cut to reach only the minimum standards but as a stepping stone for the improvement of health and safety in your organisation. A checklist is provided in Appendix 1 to record your progress.

7. The information contained in this book is intended as a general guide based upon legislation at time of going to press. Neither the sponsors, its staff nor the authors can accept liability for any loss arising as a result of reliance upon any information contained herein. Readers are strongly advised to obtain professional advice on an individual basis.

CHAPTER 1

Duty of care

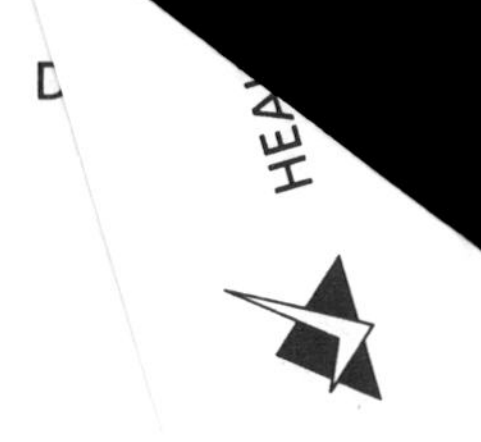

Duty of Care

An important concept in health and safety is 'duty of care', which is a general legal duty on both individuals and organisations to avoid carelessly causing personal injury or damage to property. This is a duty in common law* which we all owe to our fellow human beings. For employers, this has been developed and extended by health and safety legislation. Details of the basic legal requirements with regard to health and safety are outlined throughout this book.

LIABILITY

If someone (the plaintiff) suffers injury, loss or damage because a person or persons (the defendant(s)) were negligent (at fault), the plaintiff can claim damages from the defendant(s) if they can prove negligence by showing that:

- they were owed a duty of care by the defendant
- the duty of care was broken
- the injury, loss or damage suffered by the plaintiff occurred as a result.

The standard is that of reasonable care and generally, it can be said that the greater the risk, the higher the standard of care which is required.

The part of the law covering damages (compensation) is civil law, which is concerned with the legal rights of the individual. There are legal requirements regarding having insurance to cover certain compensation liabilities (for example drivers must have as a minimum third party insurance – this is covered in more detail in chapter 4).

ORGANISATIONS WITH EMPLOYEES

Employers have a statutory duty to take care of employees and others under statute law†, which is concerned with rights and wrongs in society. If they break their duty of care, they can be tried in a criminal court and, if found guilty, charged a fine or in serious cases, sent to prison.

'Employees' are individuals working full or part time, doing manual, clerical or any other kind of work, who have a contract of employment with the employer. This applies whether the contract is written, or agreed verbally.

In the event of an accident, an employer can be found to be criminally liable and ordered to pay a fine, as well as being civilly liable and obliged to pay damages. While organisations can insure against claims for damages through negligence, they cannot insure against the punishment and the payment of fines. Note also that employers have 'vicarious' liability for acts of negligence by employees, which means the employer could be liable even if they did not authorise the employee's act or knew nothing about it.

* *Generally, the common law relates to non-statute made law as a result of decisions made by judges in cases.*

† *Statute relates to an Act of Parliament and statute law is the body of enacted law or legislation together with the accompanying judicial decisions which explains individual statutes.*

ORGANISATIONS WITH VOLUNTEERS ONLY

Organisations with volunteers will not be held criminally liable under employment law, as they are not bound by these laws. However, they could be found criminally liable under other laws, for example if they own their premises or if they are the sole occupants, they could be found criminally negligent for breaking the duty associated with their occupancy (see chapter 8 on fire procedures).

In general, for organisations with volunteers only, liability is based on common law duty of care. If a volunteer is asked to do a task which results in them injuring themselves, the members of the governing body may be liable. For example, if the volunteer was injured whilst lifting a client out of a chair, the organisation could be found to be negligent if the volunteer had not been given suitable training on how to lift or assistance was not available to help lift the client.

In this context, consideration will be given to the system of work. It might also be argued that voluntary organisations have not met their duty of care if they have failed to keep up with relevant literature. Employers are clearly under a duty to obtain and keep up with relevant literature (eg. guidance from the HSE), but the same may also be said of voluntary organisations.

Even if volunteers have themselves been negligent, the members of the governing body could still be liable if they have not acted reasonably in training or supervising the volunteer. For example, if a volunteer drove a vehicle on the organisation's business and after an accident it was discovered that the volunteer did not have a full driving licence, the members of the governing body could be liable for not checking the volunteer's licence. The notion of duty of care needs to be considered in all aspects of an organisation's work and activities.

In the event of litigation (going to court), each case is decided individually on its merits and the particular circumstances, although case law (i.e. what has happened in similar cases before) may be referred to in evidence. The amount of effort members of the governing body have put towards assessing the likelihood of possible events occurring, and the preventative action they have taken, will be relevant in deciding whether or not they have been negligent (see chapter 6 on risk assessment). An example might be checking the criminal record of all volunteers working with vulnerable clients and taking relevant action, such as refusing to allow a person to become a volunteer who does not agree to be vetted under the Childrens' Act.

In order to protect your organisation, you are advised to follow good practice, and ensure that:

- members of your governing body and everyone involved in the organisation's activities understand the relevant parts of the law and their duty of care to everyone who uses the organisation's premises, makes use of its products and services or takes part in its activities;

- employees, volunteers and others who carry out the organisation's activities are properly recruited, inducted, trained and supervised;
- you have clearly defined the nature and limits of tasks that employees and volunteers carry out, making it clear when authority must be obtained;
- suitable records are kept of all incidents involving personal injury, loss or damage, (and any near misses or threats);
- your organisation has a clear procedure for dealing with complaints relating to health and safety.

When is a volunteer not a volunteer?

Recent industrial tribunals have considered people who were apparently volunteers to be employees in the eyes of the law. Organisations should be cautious about assuming people have the status of volunteer – in a recent case, a person worked four mornings a week and she was paid £40 per week for expenses, although she lived nearby, did not take lunch breaks and may not have incurred any expenses at all. The tribunal referred to these facts in deciding that the volunteer was in fact an employee as far as the law is concerned.

It is difficult to obtain a water-tight definition of a volunteer, but for the purpose of this book, a volunteer is understood to be someone who voluntarily gives their time or professional expertise for the benefit of a third party and is not, nor expects, to be rewarded in any way, other than the reimbursement of bona fide expenses.

In the Introduction, we strongly recommended that all organisations, including those without any employees, follow the requirements of health and safety legislation as outlined in this book. If you adopt the same standard of care that is owed to employees to your volunteers and members then you can be confident that in the eyes of the law you will be seen to be carrying out your health and safety duty of care in a responsible manner.

Examples of where a duty of care may arise

Duty of care can arise in many ways which may not always be apparent, for example:

- loaning equipment to others
- cleaning cars
- charity sponsored walks
- running fetes or fairs
- sporting activities such as swimming
- events involving animals
- visitors and contractors on your premises
- occupying premises
- controlling of a group on premises which you do not own
- differing standards of duties to children compared to adults.

The list is almost endless and serves as a reminder that vigilance is of the utmost importance.

CHAPTER 2

Your Health & Safety Policy

Statement of Intent

Your Health & Safety Policy

A health and safety policy is the foundation for developing health and safety practices within any organisation. The policy declares the degree of commitment that those who manage the organisation have towards the health and safety of everyone who will be involved in the organisation's activities – members of the governing body, employees, volunteers, members, users and the general public. It describes the strategies and procedures by which health and safety will be managed and names those people responsible for carrying them out.

Your safety policy should be a working document used in both induction and training of staff and volunteers. It should be revised regularly to ensure procedures are still relevant to the organisation's activities, and that they are being carried out as intended.

By Law* employers who have 5 or more employees must:

- have a written health and safety policy
- communicate it to employees and anyone else working under the organisation's control (including volunteers and contractors)
- make it available for inspection
- review it regularly.

If you have less than 5 employees, we strongly recommend that you have a health and safety policy in writing even though it is not compulsory, as it will help clarify procedures and areas of responsibility, and it should help to make people in your organisation more aware of health and safety issues.

A HEALTH & SAFETY POLICY DOCUMENT

A health and safety policy document is in three parts.

Part 1 The General Statement of Policy
This is the statement of your organisation's commitment in writing to tackle health and safety issues. It must be dated and signed.

Part 2 Responsibility for carrying out the Statement of Intent
Those persons with specific areas of responsibility, such as those in charge of fire procedures or first aid provision, should be identified.

Part 3 The Arrangements and Procedures
The systems and arrangements you have made to comply with your statement of intent will form this part of the policy, eg. your fire procedures, accident reporting, copies of risk assessments and any other specific procedures you have made.

* *The Health and Safety at Work etc. Act 1974*

The general statement of policy is a demonstration of your commitment to improving health and safety procedures and is something you can do straight away – an example is printed at the end of this chapter.

A basic health and safety policy is printed at the end of the book in Appendix 2 you can fill in part 1 now. You will start to prepare the documents to create the rest of the policy as you work through the book. Remember it is not just a case of filling in the blank spaces, you will need to have a clear strategy for establishing health, safety and welfare within your organisation.

Volunteers only

You are not obliged to produce a health and safety policy, but you still have a duty of care to volunteers. A policy will help you and your organisation to clarify procedures and areas of responsibility.

We strongly recommend you to carry out the same procedures as above to produce a policy, communicating it to volunteers and reviewing it regularly.

When you have completed this chapter, turn to the Checklist on page 104 and tick off the actions you have taken.

CHAPTER 3

Registering your Activity

Enforcement of Health & Safety

Every organisation which has paid employees must register the existence of their premises and activities, regardless of size or location. Health and safety legislation is enforced by either the Health and Safety Executive (HSE) or the Environmental Health Service Department (EHSD), which is part of the local council. The local Fire Brigade also requires notification of your existence, because they have responsibility for fire precautions (see chapter 8).

The enforcement agency with which you register is determined by the type of work in which your organisation is involved. Generally speaking, work which involves high risks, such as construction or manufacture, is enforced by the HSE and lower risk activities like retailing are looked after by the local EHSD. If you are starting a new organisation with paid staff, you should give the appropriate agency as much notice as possible before you open or begin operating. It is never too late to register, but failure to register your activity can result in a fine.

All types of activity are required to register. Even if you are only employing people to work on a temporary summer play-scheme, the location and activity will still need to be registered.

WHO SHOULD YOU REGISTER WITH?

1 For an activity involving manufacture or repair (such as clothing manufacture, furniture repair, craft making, printing or processing activities). You need to inform your local HSE. To do this, complete Form F9 and send it to your local HSE office (listed in Appendix 3). For building construction use form FIO and this should also be sent to your local HSE office.

2 For an activity involving retailing or storage, such as catering (see chapter 12 on Food Hygiene), warehousing, office work or leisure activities (see below), you should inform your local EHSD by completing form OSR1. EHSDs will be listed in your local telephone directory under the local council.

If you are unsure which category your activity falls into, ring the HSE Infoline on 0541 545500 (open 8.30am to 5.00pm, Monday to Friday).

ACTIVITIES FOR WHICH YOU MAY NEED A LICENCE

For some activities, you will require a licence from the relevant enforcement agency. For the voluntary sector, some of the most relevant ones are for entertainment and food. If you have any doubts or queries about needing a licence, contact your local EHSD or the HSE.

For example, if you are running an event where music and dancing are the main attractions you will require an entertainments licence.

- If the venue is already licensed, then the conditions of the licence must be complied with, such as the maximum numbers allowed to attend the event. You must also comply with the current fire precaution arrangements in force at the venue.
- For a venue which is not licensed (such as a building not normally used for entertainments), you must apply for a temporary entertainment licence from your Local Authority Licensing Section.

The main items of concern regarding health and safety for the granting of an entertainment licence are:

- potential fire hazards
- requirements for fire exits
- fire escape procedures
- fire fighting equipment
- the safety of electrical equipment.

For example, you decide to have a barn dance as a fundraising event, and a local farmer has agreed you can use his old barn. Your organisation would have to comply with all the above to ensure the event was held safely. Other activities for which a licence will be required include:

- an event which involves the sale of alcohol
- running an outdoor activity centre.

Volunteers only

Organisations who do not employ paid staff do not normally need to register their activity unless they are involved in a dangerous process or activity, such as putting on a fireworks display. Check with your local EHSD if you have any queries.

The following are exceptions:

- if your organisation owns or controls premises, you will need to obtain a fire certificate (see chapter 8)
- you need to register premises with the EHSD if food is prepared, stored, supplied or sold there on five or more days in any five week period. The five days do not need to be consecutive. The registration requirements also apply to food provision out of doors (see chapter 12).

When you have completed this chapter, turn to the Checklist on page 104 and tick off the actions you have taken.

CHAPTER 4

Insurance

Insurance

Every voluntary organisation whatever its size or activities should examine its insurance cover at least once a year. All too frequently it is only when an accident or other unforeseen event occurs that insurance is discussed, often because the organisation finds that it is not insured for the incident and is facing costs for liability.

RESPONSIBILITY

It is up to the members of the governing body of your organisation to make sure you have the appropriate insurance cover. Remember, legal responsibility is shared between all the members of the governing body – liability cannot be passed on to an individual member, as illustrated in the case of the Scout Council below. We recommend that a senior member of your organisation take responsibility for all insurance matters, preparing an annual insurance report for presentation to the management committee at least once a year.

In a recent tragic case, a child from a school visiting a Scout's activity centre drowned in the centre's pool. This resulted in the local Scout Council being fined £10,000 with £7,000 costs for failing to ensure the safety of visitors. The judgement was made against the entire Scout Council, not individual members of the Council.

Insurance cover should be additional to, rather than instead of action taken to reduce risks. In the above example, the Local Authority which brought the case against the Scout Council issued a statement to organisations warning them to consider the health and safety of visitors to their sites, as well as their own members and employees. It added 'it is not sufficient to assume visiting organisations will act safely, and insurance cover is no substitute for the proper control of risks'.

FINDING APPROPRIATE INSURANCE

Insurance needs for charitable organisations can be very complex. It is good advice to explain your needs to an insurance broker. There are a number of insurance companies and brokers who specialise in insuring the voluntary sector – you could ask a colleague or your local Council for Voluntary Service for a recommendation.

Although insurance policies may be obtained more cheaply by approaching insurance companies directly, a good insurance broker can take you through the endless types of insurance and costs, advising you on what risks the organisation should be insured against and advising on the policy that is best for your organisation. They will also remind you to renew your insurance and help you to make claims against your insurance policy.

Don't forget that if the activities of your organisation change, you should consult your insurance company or broker as you may need additional insurance cover.

TYPES OF INSURANCE

1 Employers' Liability Insurance

Employers' liability insurance covers your paid employees in the event of an accident, disease or injury caused or made worse as a result of work. All employers are required by law to ensure that any liability to a paid employee is covered by such insurance.

By Law* employers must:

- take out and maintain an approved insurance policy with an authorised insurer to cover paid employees, including temporary workers, part time workers, casual workers and apprentices;
- seek advice as to the extent of the insurance cover required for their activities. A minimum of £2 million is a requirement of the law, which will shortly be raised to £5 million;
- display prominently the certificate of insurance in the workplace where it can be seen by employees.

It may be necessary to treat trainees as employees for insurance purposes (especially those on Government training schemes and people serving community orders). If in any doubt talk to your insurers or project sponsors.

You should also check the insurance status of any secondees or work placements working for your organisation.

What is not covered by employers' liability insurance

- Employers' liability insurance covers only illness, injury or death caused by the employers negligence (see chapter 1). The insurance does not normally cover situations where the employer has not been found to have been negligent.
- The insurance will protect you from legal costs resulting from your inaction or negligence, and it should cover any legal costs, but it will not pay for fines.
- The insurance does not cover personal property or the organisation's contents or equipment.

Volunteers Only

In some recent legal cases, voluntary workers have been considered by industrial tribunals to be employees, and therefore entitled to the same terms and condition as paid employees, including employers' liability insurance cover. 'Employees' are any individuals working full or part time, doing manual, clerical or any other kind of work, who have a contract of employment with the employer. This applies whether the contract is written, or agreed verbally. Don't forget that paying a fixed rate for expenses rather than reimbursing actual expenses may mean a volunteer becomes an employee in law.

If there is any doubt about the legal status of your voluntary workers, you are well advised to obtain specialist advice on the matter, and you should consider seeking advice about the need for employers' liability insurance for volunteers.

* *Employers' Liability (Compulsory Insurance) Act 1969. N.B. The law does not apply to people working in Great Britain for less than 14 consecutive days a year, to close relatives of the employer, or to independent contractors engaged by the employer, nor does it apply to persons working aboroad.*

2 Public Liability Insurance

Although there is no strict legal obligation to have public liability insurance, any organisation which owns premises or arranges public events is strongly recommended to take out public liability insurance. Members of the governing body may be in breach of trust if they have control of, or own premises and do not take out public liability insurance, as they would not have discharged their duty in protecting the assets of the organisation.

This insurance covers individuals (other than employees) and organisations in the event of accident, injury or death, or damage to, or loss of property caused through the negligence of someone acting with the organisation's authority, including the actions of your volunteers.

If volunteers, trainees and members of the governing body are not explicitly included in the employers' liability insurance, they should be explicitly included in the public liability insurance – check with your insurance company.

It is a good idea to display your public liability certificate where your members can see it. You should make every organisation member aware of what the insurance policy covers and more importantly what it does not cover.

What is not covered by public liability insurance

- There are some common exclusions in public liability insurance for certain high risk activities such as aviation activities, hot air ballooning, parachute or bungee jumping. Remember if your organisation becomes involved in any new and potentially high risk activities, they may be excluded from your public liability insurance policy – check with your insurers.
- Public liability insurance does not normally cover special events – see section 5b
- The insurance does not cover personal property or the organisation's contents or equipment.

3 Personal Accident Insurance

Organisations may wish to take out personal accident insurance to cover accident or deaths arising from paid work or volunteering, but not due to the organisation's negligence. In other words, it would not matter whose fault it was if a person was injured or killed working for the organisation. A sum of money would be paid to the person injured and/or to support their dependants.

If the benefit is extended to members of the governing body, the Charity Commission's permission must first be sought.

4 Product Liability Insurance

This type of insurance covers organisations who make, manufacture, and sell or supply goods from claims made against them arising from death, illness or injury caused by products sold or supplied.

5 Other areas which need considering

a) Contractors
Contractors and self-employed personnel hired for any work with your organisation should have their own public liability insurance. This will cover your members and property against any injury or damages caused by them. You should check that they have this insurance.

b) Special events
If your organisation is planning a special event which is not part of your normal activities, for instance a fireworks display or an outing for children, you should first check if your existing insurance covers this type of event or activity. If not, think very seriously about taking out additional insurance to cover the event or activity.

c) Other persons/organisations attending your event
You are advised to ensure that all other organisations attending or supplying a service at any event you organise – such as a catering unit at a village festival – have their own valid public liability insurance policy. This will indemnify you in the event of something going wrong as a result of their activity, food poisoning for example.

d) Road vehicles
(i) Organisation's vehicles
By law, if your organisation operates its own vehicles, you must ensure that they are properly insured and only used for the purposes stated in the insurance documents.

You should read your insurance documents carefully and be aware of any exclusion clauses. Some exclusions are very common, for example drivers under 25 years of age are commonly excluded from driving minibuses unless named on the policy; people with certain medical conditions such as epilepsy or heart disease may be excluded from cover on your insurance.

Remember it is extremely important to keep your insurance company up-to-date if drivers' medical conditions change. Driving convictions also have to be notified to your insurer. Not telling your insurance company of changes could invalidate your drivers insurance.

(ii) Own vehicles
If your organisation allows or expects paid employees or volunteers to use their own motor vehicles for work purposes (called business use) such as delivering goods, driving to work-related meetings or picking up pensioners to visit a lunch club, you should make sure their motor insurance covers them for the activity.

Personnel should immediately stop using their vehicles for voluntary work until they have consulted with their individual insurance companies and established their insurance position, or until additional insurance cover is arranged.

A simple standard letter for drivers to send their insurance company can be drawn up easily. You could also produce a declaration for the driver to sign confirming that they have obtained approval from their insurance company to use their vehicle for business purposes. Yearly checks should also be made to ensure insurance cover has been renewed.

(iii) Occasional use insurance
Your organisation can arrange insurance cover for paid staff and volunteers to use their private cars on an occasional basis for the organisation's business.

(iv) No claims bonus
Your organisation may wish to consider taking out insurance to protect the no claims bonus of its drivers, while carrying out duties on behalf of the organisation. If you are a charitable organisation, then you should seek the Charity Commission's consent first.

(v) Large organisations
If your organisation has a lot of drivers, it may be prudent to take out motor contingency insurance, which provides third party cover to employees and/or volunteers if their own insurance has lapsed or been invalidated. However, remember that third party insurance provides only limited cover.

When you have completed this chapter, turn to the Checklist on page 104 and tick off the actions you have taken.

CHAPTER 5

Health, Safety & Welfare

Legislation

Health, safety and welfare legislation has been introduced to improve the working environment, to ensure that the risks to health are reduced to the lowest possible level and that a suitable and safe place for work is provided.

By law* employers must provide:

- a safe place of work i.e. clean, tidy and free from risk
- a safe system of work eg. adequate guarding of machines or proper use of chemicals
- adequate supervision – employees shall not be left to their own devices, but should be checked to ensure that they are working safely
- training and information – employees must have sufficient skills and knowledge to carry out their work safely
- a safety policy (if they employ 5 or more persons) – see chapter 2.

Legislation also places a duty on employees to:

- look after themselves and others – they must not act in an unsafe manner and put themselves or others in danger;
- cooperate with the employer in matters of health and safety – they should carry out health and safety instructions.

In addition to the Health and Safety at Work etc. Act 1974 there are six regulations introduced by the European Directives 1992 which apply to all places of work.

These are:

1. The Management of Health and Safety at Work Regulations 1992
2. The Workplace (Health, Safety and Welfare) Regulations 1992
3. The Provision and Use of Work Equipment Regulations 1992
4. The Manual Handling Operations Regulations 1992
5. The Personal Protective Equipment at Work Regulations 1992
6. The Health and Safety (Display Screen Equipment) Regulations 1992

A list of regulations, including those which apply to special risks, is provided in Appendix 4.

Volunteers Only

Organisations with volunteers only are not bound by these regulations, but they do need to ensure that their working conditions are safe. It would be hard to justify having lower standards of health and safety for volunteers compared to paid staff, simply because the law does not demand it (see Chapter 1).

* *Health and Safety at Work etc. Act 1974*

1. THE MANAGEMENT OF HEALTH & SAFETY AT WORK REGULATIONS 1992

The Management of Health & Safety at Work Regulations 1992 require that health and safety is implemented at all places of work. Employers have a duty to identify the potential risks to employees and others, assess when they could occur and who could be affected. If risks are identified, employers should take appropriate action to eliminate or minimise them.

You may have to use information from the HSE, suppliers and other sources.

By law employers must:

- identify and assess all risks of hazards associated with their activity which may have an effect on the health and safety of their employees and others;
- carry out risk assessments using persons who are competent (see chapter 6);
- take action to eliminate or reduce hazards;
- record the arrangements made if 5 or more persons are employed;
- review arrangements as and when changes occur;
- cooperate with other employers if employees share the same risk;
- provide health and safety training for employees and temporary workers.

You are advised to begin the assessments in-house, but if you have any difficulties at all, don't hesitate to ask for information or advice from outside organisations such as suppliers or the HSE Infoline on 0541 545500.

Employees also have a part to play, as they are obliged to:

- work to procedures specified
- cooperate with training and instructions given by an employer
- inform the employer of hazards at the workplace.

In this way, everyone in the workplace has a role to ensure the conditions meet the legal requirements.

2. THE WORKPLACE (HEALTH, SAFETY AND WELFARE) REGULATIONS 1992

These regulations are aimed at protecting employees' health from injury or long term illness; their safety by protection from immediate danger and their welfare by providing facilities for personal comfort at work.

The Health aspects are covered by ensuring:

- adequate ventilation eg. for workplace fumes, and toilets should be ventilated to the outside

- reasonable temperature, at least 16°C (there is no maximum)
- suitable lighting
- clean floors, walls, furniture, ceilings, windows and fittings
- adequate seating if work can be undertaken whilst sitting down
- no undue reaching, bending or stretching is required when using equipment or machinery
- enough space for each person (the minimum should be 3.7 square metres (40 square feet), of floor space; 11 cubic metres (400 cubic feet) of air space)

Safety is promoted by providing:

- safe premises, floors and stairs – floors are clean and tidy with no tripping hazards
- suitably maintained equipment or machinery
- space for safe movement of persons – people must be able to enter and leave safely
- fencing of openings from which persons are likely to fall
- safe storage for all materials and goods
- safety glass in windows where appropriate
- control of vehicles where pedestrians are at risk, eg. traffic calming measures.

The Welfare aspects are covered by providing:

- sufficient number of toilets for the number of people – consult your local EHSD
- suitable washing facilities with hot and cold water, soap and towels
- facilities if required for changing, drying and storing clothes
- accessible drinking water
- suitable facilities for rest and eating
- suitable provision for non-smokers.

3. THE PROVISION AND USE OF WORK EQUIPMENT REGULATIONS 1992

All equipment provided by the employer for use at work should comply with these regulations. The main provisions are to ensure that all work equipment shall be suitable for its purpose and used only for that purpose, maintained adequately, and restricted to only the persons given the task of using it.

Again, the key aspects are that the risks of using equipment are assessed and measures should be taken to protect against potential hazards from using the equipment, which ideally would involve eliminating the hazard, but may, as a last resort, include issuing protective equipment. Training should be provided for people using and maintaining the equipment.

4. THE MANUAL HANDLING OPERATIONS REGULATIONS 1992

This requires a risk assessment to be carried out in all cases where employees have to carry, lift, push or pull items as part of their employment.

Employers should avoid any manual handling operations which involve the risk of injury. The assessment should identify any unnecessary operations.

If an operation cannot be avoided, then employers need to take steps to reduce the risk of injury, give information about the object to be moved (such as its weight, its heaviest side) and to provide a safe system of work. The assessment needs to be reviewed periodically or when changes are made.

There is also an obligation on employees to make full use of the guidelines provided as a result of the assessment.

Manual Handling Checklist

☑ Decide whether it is possible to avoid handling the load, eg. can it be done mechanically or can a truck be used?

☑ Check whether the following are needed to carry out the job:
- special information/training
- special capabilities eg. training or experience
- personal protective equipment (see section 5). Note: personal protective clothing must allow for free movement during manual handling.

☑ Ensure specific instructions are given to persons not to lift loads if they consider the load is:
- too heavy
- too bulky/unwieldy
- too difficult to get hold of
- of a dangerous nature, eg. hot, sharp, a hazardous chemical.

☑ Those in charge should ensure people are given advice and assistance before starting the job. Consider individual circumstances, eg. those with health problems or who are pregnant.

☑ Assess whether the job involves any of the following movements (which increase the chance of injury) when carrying or lifting:
- the load is held away from the upper body
- twisting
- bending
- reaching upwards
- carrying the load on one side of the body
- carrying the load for a long distance
- too much pushing or pulling
- repetitive handling
- movements where the rate of work is governed by factors outside the operator's control eg unloading a conveyor.

☑ There must be a rest and/or recovery period.

☑ The area where the job is to be done should be free from risk, and there must be:

- ample space to allow persons to work and get to the load
- an even and level floor with no tripping or slipping hazards
- reasonable temperature/humidity and air movement
- good level of lighting.

5. THE PERSONAL PROTECTIVE EQUIPMENT AT WORK REGULATIONS 1992

This requires that adequate protective equipment and clothing must be made available where appropriate, in cases where risks to safety and health have not been controlled by other means. The regulations only apply to clothes and equipment used for health and safety reasons (uniforms and items that do not have a protective function are not included under these regulations). It is not sufficient to merely provide protective equipment without assessing the hazards in order to eliminate or reduce them.

Any personal protective equipment provided should be in good condition, replaced when found defective, stored in a suitable place when not in use, and the user should be provided with information instruction and training in its use.

The employer must take reasonable steps to ensure that the equipment is used, and employees are obliged to use it and report any loss or defect.

6. THE DISPLAY SCREEN EQUIPMENT REGULATIONS 1992

Special provisions apply to the use of Visual Display Units (VDUs) and for those employees who use VDUs as a significant part of their work. They generally only apply to desk top computer type monitors, although lap-tops are included if they are in prolonged use.

Employers must:

- provide suitable and sufficient analysis of the work station and review it if there is a change
- reduce risks identified by the assessment (see chapter 6)
- plan the activities of the users of the work station
- ensure the work is interrupted by breaks and changes to reduce the workload
- provide appropriate eye sight tests to be completed by a competent person at regular intervals (every two years is generally considered to be reasonable)
- supply corrective glasses if required
- provide training and information to ensure persons are not exposed to unnecessary risks.

The assessment should cover such risks as upper limb disorder (also known as RSI). HSE guidance acknowledges that there are difficulties in predicting the likelihood of musculo-skeletal problems, but suggests users are encouraged to report any relevant symptoms at an early stage.

The regulations do not acknowledge that there is a link between using VDUs and pregnancy problems, however, the possibility of a risk has not been ruled out. The regulations only suggest that you discuss the issue with pregnant women to reduce stress or anxiety, but in our opinion it would be good practice to provide alternative work if possible.

VDU Checklist

The use of visual display equipment should not be a source of risk to users. The following conditions must be achievable on computer systems to prevent risks to health.

The Equipment

☑ **Display Screen**

- The screen image should be stable with no flickering.
- The brightness/contrast control should be easily adjusted.
- The screen must tilt and swivel easily.
- The screen height must be adjustable.
- The screen must be free from glare.
- The screen should be regularly cleaned.

☑ **Keyboard**

- The keyboard should be adjustable to allow a comfortable working position.
- There must be sufficient space in front of the keyboard to support the users hands.

☑ **Work Desk**

- The work desk should be large enough to allow flexibility in positioning all of the equipment.
- The surface shall not cause reflective glare.
- A document holder should be available, if needed.

☑ **Work Chair**

- The chair shall be stable.
- It must allow the operator freedom of movement.
- The height of the chair must be adjustable.
- The back must be adjustable for both height and tilt.
- A footrest must be provided if required.

The Work Environment

☑ **Space Requirements**

- There must be sufficient space provided around the workstation.

☑ **Lighting**

- The lighting has to be satisfactory and suitable for the vision requirements of the user.
- Disturbing glare and reflection on the display screen from light fittings, windows and walls shall be avoided.

☑ **Power**

- Cables shall not provide tripping hazards.
- Sufficient electrical sockets shall be available to prevent overloading and unnecessary trailing cables.

☑ **Noise**

- The equipment noise should be low and not distract attention or disturb normal speech.

Heat Emission and Radiation

☑ The heat emitted from the equipment must be dissipated equally in the work environment and not cause concentrated hot spots.

The Software

☑ The software should be easy to understand. If possible, the software should allow the pace of work to be varied.

The Users

☑ Training is required on:

- use of the workstation
- health and safety relative to the workstation
- ergonomics.

Users need to:

- understand eye and eyesight testing
- be aware of changes in eye discomfort, especially if contact lenses are worn, and seek advice as soon as the change is noticed
- understand that regular work breaks must be taken when there are lengthy periods at the VDU.

The details covered above are not comprehensive, but they do give you a good idea of the areas which need to be considered. You need to assess your own premises and work activities, preferably with input from all who use the equipment, and outside advisors where necessary (you can contact the HSE Infoline on 0541 545500).

When you have completed this chapter, turn to the Checklist on page 104 and tick off the actions you have taken.

When you have completed this chapter, turn to the Checklist on page [illegible] and tick off the actions you have taken.

CHAPTER 6

Risk Assessment

What is Risk Assessment?

Risk assessment is a requirement of the Management of Health and Safety at Work Regulations 1992. If you have more than five employees the risk assessments have to be written down. We recommend these are included in the Arrangements section of your health and safety policy. If you employ less than five people, you are still obliged to carry out assessments, but you do not have to record them in writing. However, we strongly recommend that you do so, as they define responsibilities, and they may help to make people in your organisation more aware of health and safety.

- A hazard is anything that has the potential to cause harm (eg. a slippery floor).
- Risk is the likelihood of a hazard causing harm.

Taking the dictionary definition of safety as meaning something free from risk is misleading. Nothing can be absolutely free from risk, therefore nothing can be absolutely safe. However, there are degrees of risk, and the Health and Safety at Work etc. Act 1974 requires that risk is reduced to a level as low as reasonably practicable*. Risk assessment is the technique used to achieve this.

Risk assessment involves:

- identifying the hazards resulting from the organisation's activities that could affect anyone, including members of the governing body, employees, volunteers and the general public
- assessing the risk of the hazards occurring
- evaluating the likely severity of the outcome
- eliminating the hazards if possible, or else reducing them to the lowest level of risk that is reasonably practicable.

CARRYING OUT A RISK ASSESSMENT

Assessing risk requires detailed knowledge of the working practices normally only found in people who are experienced in doing the work. We believe that assessing risk cannot be properly done without the cooperation and involvement of your employees and volunteers. Remember you also have a duty to consult with safety representatives (see Chapter 14) – they have often received excellent health and safety training and will be able to assist you in joint risk assessments. You may also need to request specialist help (the HSE can offer advice-contact their Infoline on 0541-545500).

There is no overall formula for rating risks, but the main factors you have to take into account are:

- the nature of the hazard
- the likelihood of it occurring
- how often it may occur
- how the hazard could affect health or safety
- the working environment, eg. lifting heavy weights could be more of a risk in a cold and wet environment

* *What is reasonably practicable will vary depending on the circumstances, but you have to evaluate the risk of the hazards happening, the number of people it may affect and the cost of remedying the problem. Seek advice from the HSE if you are in any doubt. You are entitled to take into account the cost, although there are no guidelines on how to evaluate the costs against safety gains.*

- the number of employees, volunteers or members of the public who could be affected
- potentially vulnerable people such as the young, elderly or disabled.

The results of the risk assessment will be useful in determining gaps in skills or knowledge in your organisation, and identify training needs. There are five steps to risk assessment shown below.

Step 1 Look for potential hazards

When doing the assessment, you should walk around your premises with an employee/ volunteer, or safety representative if available, and take a critical look at your surroundings to see what could potentially cause harm or injury to any staff, volunteers or members of the public. Don't forget to ask other people's opinion in this process – they may mention problems you are not aware of, and involving them in the process usually means that they will be more committed to the outcome.

As a simple example, as you are walking round, you might notice one of your volunteers reaching under a table to disconnect a hot kettle in order to plug in a printer. You realise that this is a hazard which could result in an accident – the volunteer could be scalded by hot water; they could hit their head on the table or water could go into the electrical socket.

Step 2 Determine who can be harmed

In this case, anyone reaching under the table could be potentially at risk.

Step 3 Establish procedure to eliminate or reduce the risk of the hazard (ie control measure)

The kettle could be moved to another location, preferably with a socket above it. Ensure that plugs are easily accessible if used for more than one purpose.

Step 4 Record your findings and action taken, and inform all staff and volunteers

This helps to ensure that the action taken deals adequately with the hazard. It is also important to ensure everyone is aware of any changes made. An example is the table below.

Hazard	Control Measure	Effect
Scalding from the kettle	Re-locate the kettle to a safer position	By moving the kettle the scalding hazards have been eliminated
Water splashing into electrical socket	Plug kettle in a socket which is above the height of the kettle	The danger of water splashing onto the socket is reduced
Banging head on table	If measures above are implemented the risk will no longer occur	Risk no longer present

Step 5 Review procedures to record any incident or accident

These will help to monitor the effectiveness of the risk assessment and the action taken.

You should repeat the above exercise regularly to account for any changes or new practices. A risk assessment should be carried out for each of your activities or events.

The findings of your risk assessments and the action required to reduce the problem should be included in the Arrangements Section of your Health and Safety Policy.

Example 2

Your organisation is loaned a farm trailer to be used as a stage/ platform at a local show – it is intended that entertainers and competition prize winners will stand on the trailer in order that the public can get a good view.

A risk assessment was carried out to identify the possible risks and the findings are recorded below:

Hazard	Control Measure	Effect
Trailer moves when people are on it	Blocks and chocks under the wheels	Trailer will be prevented from moving
People tripping when on the trailer	Inspect for tripping hazards and remove them	The chance of tripping is reduced
People falling off the trailer	Build barriers at back and the side of trailer; only have the front of the trailer open. Draw a line 1 metre from the front edge of the trailer and instruct people not to step forward of the line	People cannot fall off sides or back. If people stand behind the 1 metre line, this will reduce the chance of falling off the front.
People falling whilst climbing onto the trailer	Erect stable stairway with handrail, preferably on both sides	Allows people to climb safely whilst holding the rail
People falling from stage into crowd	Build barrier 5 metres away from front of platform	Keeping audience back prevents injury caused by persons falling onto them
Persons, especially children, climbing on trailer when not in use	Remove stairway if possible when not in use. Build barrier around trailer to prevent access or mount a security guard to prevent children from playing on it	Removing the stairway and building barriers prevents easy access Maintaining security vigilance decreases the chance of access

Example 3

A group of volunteers and paid helpers have arranged to take special needs children on an outing to a local shopping centre.

Step 1 Look for potential hazards

- Lack of wheelchair access which may cause the children to become agitated or distraught.
- No lifts or escalators, which means the carers have to carry the children upstairs.
- Lack of parking space close to the centre may lead to carers having to engage in heavy lifting and children travelling over long distances, increase the likelihood of children getting lost and becoming agitated.

Step 2 Determine who can be harmed

The risks to both children and helpers need to be considered.

Step 3 Establish procedure to eliminate or reduce the risk of the hazard (ie control measure)

- Discussions were held with the carers, the guardians and the children about the arrangements for the trip.
- Each shop in the location of the shopping area was assessed for disability access and security.
- A central meeting point in the shopping area and a scheduled time to meet was arranged for all members of the party in charge of children.
- The ratio of carers to children was worked out depending on the needs of each child.
- Permission was sought for the trip and approved by the children's parents and guardians.
- Parking was pre-arranged.
- The stores were informed of the visit in advance.
- Other organisations who had arranged similar trips were contacted and consulted.
- On the day of the trip all carers were briefed and given the mobile telephone number of the trip supervisor in case of problems.

Step 4 Record your findings and action taken, and inform all staff and volunteers

Hazard	Control Measure	Effect
Lack of access to shops may lead to children becoming agitated. Carers as a result may have to carry children in to shop or upstairs.	Each shop in the location of the shopping area was assessed for disability access and security. This was discussed and agreed with the children before the trip.	Only shops with access for disabled people will be visited. Carers will not be required to lift children and the children will not become frustrated or disruptive.
Danger of children becoming lost.	A central meeting point in the shopping area and scheduled time to meet was arranged. On the day of the trip all carers were briefed on what time the group was to meet for the return journey home and given the mobile telephone number of the trip supervisor in case of problems.	Action taken should minimise the risk of children becoming lost.
Parking may not be available, requiring the children to walk or be assisted over a long distance.	Parking pre-booked.	Problem solved.
Problems with parent/guardian in the event of an incident.	Having carried out the risk assessment, parents/guardians were consulted and their permission sought.	The parents/guardians will be aware that you are taking all the reasonable precautions to ensure the safety of their child.
Claim for damages in the event of an incident.	Check that your activity is covered by your insurance.	Even though you have taken all the precautions, in the event of an incident you will be covered for injury, damage or losses.

Note: there are no hard and fast rules for carrying out a risk assessment – you need to consider the particular circumstances.

Volunteers Only

Organisations with only volunteers are not strictly required by law to carry out risk assessment, but they are strongly advised to adopt the same risk assessment methods explained in this section.

You should be aware that you have a legal responsibility of duty of care (see chapter 1).

A risk assessment will outline where action is needed and where priorities lie, so an organisation can decide where to concentrate time and resources when beginning to develop their health and safety procedures.

Organisations with both employees and voluntary workers are morally, if not legally obliged to provide the same standards of protection to volunteers as enjoyed by employees.

When you have completed this chapter, turn to the Checklist on page 104 and tick off the actions you have taken.

CHAPTER 7

Control of Substances Hazardous to Health (COSHH) Assessments

COSHH Regulations

All workplaces with employees must carry out an assessment under the Control of Substances Hazardous to Health (COSHH) Regulations 1994, which require every employer to assess the workplace for risks to health from substances used at the workplace. They must take all necessary steps to control any risk identified. The assessment, if not already done, should be carried out immediately to comply with the regulations.

WHAT IS A HAZARDOUS SUBSTANCE?

A hazardous substance can be a liquid, solid, dust, powder or gas which can damage health when it: comes into contact with skin or eyes; enters the body through the skin; is breathed in, swallowed or even transferred to the mouth via contaminated hands.

Many substances used or generated at work are hazardous to health. Working procedures should aim to minimise the effects of these substances on the health of all employees. You need to consider the possible ill-effects of all substances in use – assessment is the key.

You must then prevent your employees being exposed to hazardous substances by using less harmful substitutes or different methods of work to reduce the risk where possible.

Any substance can be potentially dangerous in certain circumstances. For instance some common household bleaches, when mixed with certain other household cleaners, can give off a poisonous gas which is extremely dangerous in confined spaces. Substances such as pesticides, wood dusts and solvent paints may not cause immediate harm but may lead to serious disease in later life. Suppliers of substances must provide hazard data sheets where requested. These will list safety precautions to be taken when using their products.

Hazard data sheets and the label on the product container or wrapping should show one of the following hazardous signs indicating the main hazards:

TOXIC

CORROSIVE

HIGHLY FLAMMABLE

EXPLOSIVE

HARMFUL

OXIDISING

CARRYING OUT THE ASSESSMENT

In many organisations, there are no really hazardous chemicals present, so a COSHH assessment would be quite straightforward. For example, if your organisation only uses mild cleaning agents, then you would need to ensure that anyone likely to use them were fully aware of any potential hazards, of how to store the substances and deal with spillages and so on.

The HSE's step-by-step guidance booklet 'COSHH Assessments' recommends that if possible, the assessment process should be started in-house, using the expertise of people doing the work. Remember that you have a duty to consult with safety representatives (see Chapter 14); they have often received excellent health and safety training and will be able to assist you in a joint risk assessments. Depending on the type and nature of the work you undertake, an outside specialist may be required to help you make your assessment (the HSE can offer advice).

A COSHH assessment should use the same steps as used above for risk assessment to determine the precautions required to protect the health of employees and others exposed to substances. The COSHH regulations set out essential measures that the employer and employees have to take. In order to comply you have to follow the steps below.

Step 1 Look for potential hazards

- Identify hazardous substances present.
- Consider the risks they present to people's health if the risk is significant.

Step 2 Determine who can be harmed

Step 3 Establish procedure to eliminate or reduce the risk of the hazard

- Exposure to a hazardous substance such as photocopier toner or solvent-based paints should be prevented if possible by providing a safer alternative, or else limited by improving ventilation, reducing the number of people exposed or providing appropriate protective equipment.
- Training should be provided as required and, in cases where exposure to substances is linked to particular diseases or adverse health affects, and there is reasonable likelihood of these occurring, health surveillance will be necessary.

Step 4 Record your findings and action taken, and inform all staff and volunteers

- Any action taken should be recorded, and should be monitored to ensure control measures are used and maintained. Employees should be properly informed and trained on the dangers of the substance, risks involved and precautions to be taken. They should also be adequately supervised, and informed of the results of any exposure monitoring and emergency procedures.

Step 5 Establish procedures to record any incident or accident

- Records should be kept of any incidents or accidents to help determine what went wrong in order that appropriate action can be taken to prevent reoccurrence.

AN EXAMPLE OF A COSHH ASSESSMENT.

You are a committee member of a cricket club with garaging for machinery used for ground maintenance. The floor of the garage you intend to use the garage for a function in the event of bad weather. You find a container of caustic soda (sodium hydroxide) stored on a shelf, which was obtained from a local chemical cleaning material supplier. The label indicates that it can be used as a degreasing agent, however, there are hazardous warning signs on the container. Your COSHH assessment would be as follows.

Step 1 Look for potential hazards

The instructions refer to a safety data sheet which you can obtain from the supplier. The data sheet shows that caustic soda is corrosive and causes severe injuries if it comes into contact with the eyes, is inhaled or ingested as a dust, or comes into contact with the skin. Clearly caustic soda is hazardous to health if its use is not controlled.

Step 2 Determine who can be harmed

Anyone using the soda will be at risk, but so will anyone coming into contact with it who is unaware of its hazards, including children or animals. (Your method of working will need to include a control method to reduce the risk to children and others affected by the task).

Step 3 Establish procedure to eliminate or reduce the risk of the hazard

Firstly you try to avoid using the soda by using something else; your chemical supplier may have an alternative which is less hazardous, and needs less control on its use. You may find a product in a retail shop or superstore, but make sure this product is not hazardous. The supplier has a duty to provide information on hazardous products when requested. After considering all the alternatives, you decide that the caustic soda is actually the best product for the job.

Note: If you choose a less hazardous alternative you still have to carry out the COSHH assessment.

You now have to consider ways to reduce the risks associated with using caustic soda.

From the supplier's safety data sheet you will find information on:

- the hazards identified with the product
- first aid measures
- fire fighting measures
- accidental release measures
- handling and storage
- exposure control and personal protection
- the physical and chemical properties
- the stability and how it reacts with other products
- toxicological information
- effects on the environment
- disposal
- transport information
- regulatory information regarding labelling and safety phrases.

You note from the handling and storage information that: good ventilation is required; the substance can give off hydrogen if it comes into contact with aluminium or zinc; the substance reacts violently with acids and chlorinated hydrocarbons; a respiratory dust mask, goggles, PVC gloves, overalls and wellington boots must be worn when handling the substance.

Based on this information you tackle the job in a manner which allows the safe use of caustic soda. This will require the following precautions to be taken:

- the work is carried out on a still day, with doors and windows open
- containers and tools used are not aluminium or zinc
- the substance is only mixed with water, not with any other chemical
- a suitable dust mask is worn
- goggles and PVC gloves are worn at all times, and if using very large amounts then overalls and wellington boots are to be worn.

Step 4 Record your findings and the action taken, and inform all staff and volunteers

There are no approved COSHH forms so we have devised the following as an example.

Control of Substances Hazardous to Health (COSHH) Regulations 1994	
Company	The Boulevard Cricket Club
Hazardous Substance	Caustic soda solid (sodium hydroxide solid)
Supplier	Chemicals-Are-Us Ltd
Manufacturer	United Unassociated Chemicals
Description of Task	Cleaning ingrained oil residues from floor
Number of persons involved	One
Type of potential exposure: Eyes Inhalation Skin	 Yes Yes Yes
Risk Classification	Corrosive Irritant
Other Hazards	Reacts with zinc and aluminium
Control Measures	Use with good ventilation inside Do not use on a windy day
Personal Protective Equipment	Use PVC overall and wellington boots, goggles and PVC gloves at all times
Training	Person must be trained how to control hazard and what to do in an emergency
First Aid: **Eye Contact**	 Wash thoroughly with water for at least 10 mins. Seek immediate medical attention.
Skin Contact	Drench skin with plenty of water. Remove contaminated clothing and wash before reuse. If large area of irritation persists, seek medical attention.
Inhalation	Remove from exposure, rest and keep warm. In severe cases, or where recovery is not rapid or complete, seek medical attention.
Ingestion	Wash out mouth with water. Do not induce vomiting. If patient is conscious give water to drink. If patient feels unwell seek medical attention.

Step 5 Establish procedures to record any incident or accident

It is important that assessments are reassessed and reviewed. When new persons are tackling the job for the first time, adequate training must be given. It is also vital that any accidents or near misses are recorded and investigated.

See chapter 10 on recording and reporting of sickness, incidents and accidents.

Please note: this is merely an example of how a COSHH Assessment is carried out. We stress that this is to show the procedure and that we do not offer this as an approved way of removing stains from garage floors or using caustic soda.

COSHH SUMMARY

All employers must carry out Control of Substances Hazardous to Health (COSHH) Assessments

They must:

- identify hazardous substances in the workplace
- identify who is at risk from these substances
- evaluate the risk

Where possible the hazardous substance should be substituted with a safer substance. If this is not possible its use must be controlled.

We strongly recommend that the following leaflet is obtained from HSE: *COSHH: the new brief guide for employers (guidance on the main requirements of the Control of Substances Hazardous to Health (COSHH) Regulations 1994)'*, HSE Books, ISBN 0 7176 1189 2.

Volunteers only

Organisations with only volunteers are not strictly required by law to carry out COSHH assessment, but they are strongly advised to adopt the same risk assessment methods explained in this section to meet their legal responsibility of duty of care (see chapter 1).

Carrying out COSHH assessments will help you to investigate all substances used, highlight potential hazards, outline where action is needed, and where priorities lie, so an organisation can decide where to concentrate time and resources when beginning to develop their health and safety procedures.

Organisations with both employees and voluntary workers are morally, if not legally obliged to provide the same standards of protection to volunteers enjoyed by employees.

When you have completed this chapter, turn to the Checklist on page 104 and tick off the actions you have taken.

CHAPTER 8

Fire Certificate & Procedures

The Fire Certificate

All organisations must make arrangements to assess the risk of fire to both people and property and steps should be taken to minimise those risks. Fire can be costly to any organisation, even if no-one is injured, but may be more devastating to a voluntary organisation with limited resources.

By law*:

- All premises to which members of the public have access must have a fire certificate or an exemption certificate issued by the local Fire Brigade.
- Once a certificate has been issued, a copy should be kept on the premises.
- The Fire Brigade may decide that you qualify for exemption. This may be the case where premises are considered to be of low risk. The exemption will be given to you in writing. However, you still need to do a risk assessment (see next section).

WHO SHOULD APPLY FOR THE FIRE CERTIFICATE ?

- If you ***own or are the sole tenant/leaseholder*** of the premises, you as the owner or leaseholder must apply for a fire certificate.
- If you ***use premises which are not fully owned or leased to you,*** the owner of the premises is responsible for applying for the fire certificate and introducing those procedures specified in the fire certificate for the premises. However, it is the duty of each user of the premises to ensure that the fire certificate requirements are met for the areas for which they are responsible.

If you are responsible for the fire procedures, you should contact the local Fire Brigade to enquire about a fire certificate. The Brigade will send out a fire safety officer who will advise you on your fire procedures and other needs.

When the certificate is issued it will give details of:

- the use of the premises
- means of escape in case of fire
- fire fighting equipment required.

The certificate may also include details on any other fire precautions to be taken, fire drills, training and record keeping.

In addition, the Fire Precautions (Workplace) Regulations 1997 place a duty on you to carry out a risk assessment of the fire hazards of your organisation's premises. The regulations apply to all places of work.

* *The Fire Precautions Act 1971*

FIRE RISK ASSESSMENT

The purpose of the fire risk assessment is to identify fire hazards and to take action to remove or reduce the likelihood of fire being caused by those hazards. Important elements of the assessment would include ensuring access to fire exits is kept clear, and fire alarms and equipment are checked and serviced regularly.

Example

You have a small office with only one door, and you notice that there are cigarette ends in the cardboard box used for waste paper. You also notice that the water fire extinguisher is on the other side of the room to the door and that it is partially behind a cupboard. You notice that the electrical cable on the electric radiator is cracked.

Hazard	Control Measure	Effect
Cigarette ends in the waste container – risk of fire if not extinguished properly.	Ban smoking altogether or make alternative arrangements for smokers to use another room.	By banning smoking in the room, there will be no risk of the cigarette ends igniting the waste paper.
Cardboard box used for waste paper storage – risk that if there is a fire the box will also ignite, adding to the problem.	Replace with a metal container which will keep the burning contents inside.	The fire will be contained, and allow easier fire fighting.
Position of water extinguisher – risk that in the event of fire, persons will have to use the extinguisher inside the room.	Fire extinguishers must be fixed to the wall and located at the entrance to the room. Training in the use of the specific extinguisher needs to be given.	Fire can be tackled from a safe position with the operator being able to escape.
Electrical lead damaged casing.	Place a sign preventing use of the lead until changed – do not use until replaced. Institute a procedure so that regular inspections are made and records are kept. The inspections to be carried out by a person who is competent to do so.	Electrical equipment will be inspected on a regular basis, thereby eliminating the chance that a hazard is missed.

A list of common fire hazards which could be present is given below:

- flammable liquids such as cleaning fluids
- flammable gases such as aerosols
- electrical equipment producing red heat – fires, toasters, grills
- damaged electrical flexes
- overloading of electrical sockets
- storage of materials near sources of ignition
- smoking and matches
- emergency heating and lighting – portable gas fires, candles.

Having carried out the risk assessment and taken steps to eliminate or reduce the likelihood of the hazard causing an accident to the lowest reasonably practicable level, the employer then must inform or train all staff (including employees and volunteers) in the nature of the remaining hazards to enable them to be safe. An emergency plan should be introduced, and staff should be trained in it. An adequate number of persons who are competent should be appointed to assist in the plan – their competency will be determined by them having sufficient training, experience, knowledge and skill to properly perform their duties.

Don't forget that contractors and visitors must also be made aware of your emergency procedures.

If your activities involve hiring a hall or premises you should ensure the premises comply with the Fire Regulations and you should familiarise yourself and everyone else in your organisation with the fire procedures. Depending on the type of activity, you may also have responsibility for other people involved – for example, if you run a coffee morning in the local village hall, you must ensure that anyone attending is made aware of the fire procedures (by posters or signs).

Procedures in the Event of Fire

There is a duty on all persons in charge of organisations to ensure that their members have knowledge of:

- the action to be taken on discovering a fire
- what the fire alarm signal is
- what to do when the alarm is heard
- where their nearest fire exits are
- the location of their fire assembly point
- how to call the fire brigade
- the roll call procedure
- special provision required for people with mobility difficulties
- restrictions on using lifts or escalators
- conditions for re-entry to the building.

In addition to the above you will also need to ensure that:

- alarms, if fitted, are checked regularly
- fire fighting equipment is checked regularly and kept in place
- fire exits are kept unlocked and clear during occupancy
- there is clear access to fire extinguishers, alarms and exits at all times
- fire doors are kept closed
- fire exit signs are in place and not covered up.

If your organisation requires people to attempt to extinguish fires, you must ensure that they are trained to use the equipment provided. You must also ensure that they are able to assess that it is safe to do so.

The Regulations are enforced by the local Fire Brigade. Contact them (telephone number in your local telephone book) for advice about your fire risks and requirements.

When you have completed this chapter, turn to the Checklist on page 104 and tick off the actions you have taken.

CHAPTER 9

Violence in the Workplace

Violence to Staff and Volunteers

Staff and volunteers in the voluntary sector often work with vulnerable individuals and disadvantaged sections of society, and may therefore be at risk of threats or violence from the very people they care for. Staff and volunteers are often expected to face their attacker and in some cases continue to provide care for them.

You should not underestimate the effect that verbal abuse, threats or actual violence can have on staff and volunteers – working with such threats can be extremely uncomfortable and demoralising unless they feel well-equipped to deal with such situations. Training, advice and support from other members of the organisation can help alleviate the effects of violence.

By law employers must:

- report all violent incidents which lead to a major injury, three days absence from work, or if the person assaulted or involved in the incident is unable to do their normal work for three days as a result of the incident*;
- undertake a systematic general examination of all their work activities† (including the threat of violence to staff) and record the significant findings of their assessment.

You have to consider whether the work your organisation is doing has the potential to place staff in a position where they could become a victim of violent behaviour. Don't forget violent behaviour is not just physical assault. The Health and Safety Executive have defined violence as 'Any incident in which an employee is abused, threatened or assaulted by a member of the public in circumstances arising out of the course of his or her employment'.

Volunteers, although not generally covered under the above regulations will have some legal protection under duty of care. They do not enjoy the full protection of current health and safety law, but they should expect to have at least the same degree of protection and care as employees.

The benefits of developing an effective policy for preventing and dealing with violence extend far beyond any statutory duty. Staff and volunteers who are properly trained, confident and well supported are better prepared to handle difficult situations and likely to be more effective in carrying out their work.

---

* *since 1st April 1996, the Reporting of Injuries, Diseases and Dangerous Occurances Regulations (RIDDOR) – see chapter 12 – have included violence or threat of violence to staff at work*

† *Management of Health and Safety at Work Regulations, 1992*

WHAT YOU SHOULD DO

You first need to establish whether violence or the threat of violence is a problem in your workplace. An assessment will help to clarify areas where there may be shortcomings, identify potential problem areas, or simply put your mind at rest.

The general perception in your organisation may well be that you don't have a problem with violence, but remember there may be a greater threat of violence in some areas of work or at different times.

As an example, during the youth club session on a late Sunday afternoon a number of youth club members are showing aggressive behaviour to others. For whatever reason, the children have clearly been drinking and turn up at the youth club and disrupt the activities of the other children. The Sunday staff are almost all volunteers and don't usually have much contact with the management. They are nervous and unsure of how to deal with the situation.

In order to prevent this happening in the future, you should undertake an assessment of how your staff and volunteers feel about the threat of violence or verbal abuse – you may wish to include the issue of bullying in the survey. This could take the form of a simple questionnaire drawn up with staff and volunteers and/or a safety representative. The issue of confidentiality should also be discussed. It is important to include all members of staff and volunteers, particularly those who don't see you regularly. Alternatively your organisation may wish to hold a meeting to discuss the matter before you take any action.

Remember staff and volunteers need to feel confident that any answers they give will not be regarded as a sign of personal or professional failure. Remind everyone that not reporting violence, threats or verbal abuse can potentially expose other staff members and volunteers, who may be less skilled in defusing potentially violent situations, to serious risk.

You should use the results of assessment to determine whether you need to take action to reduce the incidents of violence. Safety representatives should be consulted (see chapter 13) and they can help you to develop the organisation's policy. Clearly the organisation cannot guard against all eventualities, nor can action by the employer alone bring the problem under control. But to minimise the threat of violence, it is very important to discuss the result of the assessment with all staff and volunteers. Any policy which is not jointly developed by staff and volunteers is unlikely to have their support or commitment and will be less effective.

Step 1 Look for potential hazards

Develop a questionnaire with staff, volunteers and the safety representative, if available, to determine the potential for violence in your workplace.

Step 2 Determine who can be harmed

Who are, or could be, at risk from threats or violence?

Step 3 Establish procedure to eliminate or reduce the risk of the hazard (ie control measure)

If a problem has been identified, look for ways to reduce the threat of violence. You could ensure that people work in pairs, or train your personnel to recognise potentially violent situations. Make sure you equip people to defuse violent situations.

Set up a formal reporting system to investigate incidents of threats and violence.

Step 4 Record your findings and action taken, and inform all staff and volunteers

Step 5 Review procedures to record any incident or accident

Investigate with staff and volunteers any reported incidents of violence. Ensure this investigation is used in developing policy to prevent incidents re-occurring. Policies on preventing or dealing with violence should be reviewed regularly to check their effectiveness.

Don't go over the top. The HSE in their leaflet *'Violence to Staff'* recommend trying to balance the risks to your employees against any possible side effects to the public. An atmosphere that suggests employees are worried about violence can sometimes increase its likelihood.

We have included two forms for your use to record violent incidents – you may wish to adapt them to the needs of your group.

Don't forget your clients may be vulnerable too; from their relatives, friends, neighbours, volunteers or even your own staff members. However, this book is primarily concerned about the health and safety of staff and volunteers. We advise any group working with vulnerable clients to refer to the following publications:

- *Safe and Alert: Good practice advice on volunteers working with vulnerable clients*, NCVO Publications
- *Inter-Agency Procedures Abuse of Older People in Domestic Setting*
- *Personal Safety for Health Care Workers* , P. Bibby, commissioned by the Suzy Lamplugh Trust, Arena 1995.

For further information contact the Suzy Lamplugh Trust at: 14 East Sheen Avenue, London SW14 8AS Tel: 0181 392 1839.

If the person involved in the incident is not capable of filling in this form, a senior member of staff or member of the governing body should complete the form giving relevant details as known.

Violent incident form for staff and volunteers

Block capitals please:

Date of incident: .... Time: .... Date form completed: ....

Name of person involved in incident:

Role in organisation:...Full-time ☐ Part-time ☐

Ethnicity: ....How long in organisation: ....yrs ....mths

Location at which incident occured: ....On duty ☐ Off duty ☐

What was the person involved in the incident doing at the time?

Type of incident: (you may tick more than one box)

A	Verbal threat	☐	B	Severe verbal abuse	☐
C	Racial	☐	D	Threatening posture	☐
E	Threat with weapon	☐	F	Sexual	☐
G	Physical assault	☐	H	Attempted theft	☐
I	Other	☐ (please specify)...			

Give an account in your own words of what happened and any relevant incidents leading to the incident. Attach a separate sheet if necessary, and don't worry about spelling or grammar.

....

....

....

Please include any details of any furniture or other items which may have been used in a threatening manner or were actually used in the incident.

....

....

....

Nature and extent of injuries (list all physical injuries sustained, including cuts and bruises):

....

....

....

Note: *The person involved in the incident should fill in a form for violent incidents as soon as possible.*

Violent incident form for staff and volunteers (Cont)

Emotional effects:

....

....

....

Damage to personal property including clothing:

....

....

....

Treatment given for injuries:

....

....

....

Given by: ....

Treated in hospital: .... Date:.......................................

Name of person who alerted staff to incident: ....

How long after the incident occurred?...

Name(s) of any witnesses

....

....

Occupation...

Address if not working in organisation

....

....

Name of person recording incident ....

Address

....

....

Signed .... Date:...

The details collected from employees and volunteers in this questionnaire may help in identifying areas of concern. The questions have been numbered to help in analysing the responses.

Violence Questionnaire

Male [ ] 1 Volunteer [ ] 3 Age [ ] 5 yrs

Female [ ] 2 Staff member [ ] 4

What jobs do you do? ....6 Number of hours per week.......................7

Start time.......................................8 am/pm Finish time ....9 am/pm

Do you consider the problem of violence or the threat of violence in your organisation to be:

very serious [ ] 10 minor [ ] 12

serious [ ] 11 non-existent [ ] 13

Have you ever felt threatened in your work for this organisation:

never [ ] 14 more than once [ ] 16

once [ ] 15 often [ ] 17

If yes, under what circumstances? 18

How long have you worked with us? [ ] 19 –1 year [ ] 20 – 2 years [ ] 21 + 2 years

What is your ethnic origin?

[ ] 22 White [ ] 24 Black/African [ ] 26 Black/other [ ] 28 Pakistani [ ] 30 Chinese

[ ] 23 Irish [ ] 25 Black/Caribbean [ ] 27 Indian [ ] 29 Bangladeshi Other....................31

Do you consider yourself to have a disability? Yes [ ] No [ ] 32

Are you registered disabled? Yes [ ] No [ ] 33

Briefly describe the activities you do:...34

Have you any suggestion or comments about the issues raised in this questionnaire?

....

....35

Supervisor's Report

Name:..Date form completed:.............................

I have read the report by: . ...

I recommend the following action: ....

....

....

....

....

....

Sick leave taken by member of staff/volunteer involved: ....

RIDDOR form completed: ....

Name of assailant ....

Known to organisation? Yes ☐ No ☐ .... Male ☐ Female ☐

Address: ....

....

....

Police involvement ....

Incident reported to police Yes ☐ No ☐ Charges made:...

Details: ....

Organisation response

Action to be taken ....

Entry to be made in the accident book: ....

Signed... Date: ....

When you have completed this chapter, turn to the Checklist on page 105 and tick off the actions you have taken.

CHAPTER 10

First Aid

First Aid Assessment

All employers have a duty under the law* to provide first aid facilities and equipment which is adequate and appropriate for the workplace.

By law employers must:

- make an assessment to decide what first aid facilities are adequate and appropriate for the organisation;
- provide adequate equipment and facilities.

For instance an organisation which refurbishes old gas ovens and fridges will have different first aid requirements to an organisation offering computer training to the unemployed. This is why an assessment needs to be carried out, and why the regulations do not give a definitive list, except for outlining the minimum standards all organisations have to achieve.

Factors to be considered in carrying out a first aid assessment

- Workplace hazards and risks – for instance, are there any dangerous machines or chemicals being used?
- The size of the organisation – the more personnel you have, the greater the risk of someone needing first aid.
- The organisation's history of accidents.
- The nature and distribution of the workforce – do personnel work alone or in remote areas?
- The nature of activities – the assessment of an organisation which takes parties of young children canoeing, will be very different from that of an organisation arranging school trips to the theatre. If minibuses are used, are first aid kits fitted? Are personnel trained to administer first aid?
- The availability of emergency medical services – some countryside organisations work in very remote locations.
- Employees working on shared or multi-occupied sites – it is very easy to assume the business or organisation next door will have a first aid kit or first aider.
- Holiday and other absences – absences which may leave your organisation with no first aiders and/or appointed persons.

Assessment is the key to all the above points (see also chapter 6)

After you have completed your first aid assessment, you can use the results obtained to decide on the type of first aid provision you need and the number of first aiders or appointed persons required.

You must as a minimum have someone who is able and available to take charge in an emergency. This individual is known as an APPOINTED PERSON.

An appointed person is someone who has basic first aid knowledge, and is available whenever people are at work. They can take charge in an emergency and are responsible for calling the emergency services. One-day courses are available to train appointed persons.

---

* *The Health and Safety (First Aid) Regulations 1981*

You may decide from your assessment that a trained FIRST AIDER is needed. A first aider is someone who has completed a first aid course, normally over 4 days, that is approved by the Health and Safety Executive.

Remember, although generally it is not compulsory to have a trained first aider unless there is a special hazard, they are an asset to any organisation.

TRAINING

First aiders and appointed persons have to be retrained within 3 years of their last training. You should keep records of the relevant training and retraining dates. The training should be provided by an organisation approved by the Health and Safety Executive, which could include St John's Ambulance, the Red Cross or other similar organisations.

Free help and advice on all matters of first aid is available from the Health and Safety Executive. They may also have information concerning local approved first aid courses.

FIRST AID EQUIPMENT

The assessment will also determine what first aid equipment is required.

There must be at least one first aid box, which should be in a readily accessible location and properly equipped. First aid provision should be readily available to every employee and volunteer at all times and they must be informed of its location.

There are no mandatory lists of contents of first aid boxes. Contents vary depending on the information gathered during the assessment of first aid needs. As a guide, where no special risk arises in the workplace, a minimum stock of first aid items would be:

- a leaflet giving general guidance on first aid (for example HSE leaflet)*;
- 20 individually wrapped sterile adhesive dressings (assorted sizes), appropriate to the type of work;
- two sterile eye pads;
- four individually wrapped triangular bandages (preferably sterile);
- six safety pins;
- six medium-sized individually wrapped sterile unmedicated wound dressings – approximately 12cm x 12cm;
- two large sterile individually wrapped unmedicated wound dressings – approximately 18cm x 18cm;
- one pair of disposable gloves.

**Basic advice on first aid at work IND(G)215L 1997, HSE Books ISBN 0 717610 70 5.*

There must be at least one notice telling staff:

- the location of the first aid box
- who the first aider or appointed person is
- where the first aider or appointed person can be found.

If the workplace gives rise to special hazards, eg. using a particularly toxic material, then a trained first aider may be needed – if in any doubt ask. Help is available from EHSD or HSE.

Note: In certain circumstances, for example large scale or particularly hazardous events where the risks indicate the possibility of injury, there may be a legal duty to provide first aid facilities. If in doubt, always check with the enforcement agencies.

If you are holding large events you may wish to consider having the event attended by a first aid organisation such as St Johns Ambulance. However, remember that you are responsible for assessing the first aid needs.

Volunteers only

The need to provide first aid facilities and equipment for voluntary and community based activities is covered by the general duty of care (see chapter 1).

You should always firstly undertake an assessment of the first aid needs of your whole organisation. For instance, a group which organises cricket games would not need the same first aid facilities as one which organises mountain climbing.

Examples of assessment are listed below.

- For coffee mornings an organisation decided no trained first aider was required but an appointed person should be available.
- For a large car boot sale, a trained first aider was provided.
- For a fireworks display, trained first aiders, a rest tent and ambulance were required.
- For renovation and building work done by volunteers, a trained first aider was required.
- For volunteers doing domestic gardening, an appointed person and a mobile first aid box were provided.

Remember, although generally it is not compulsory for all voluntary organisations to have a trained first aid person, they are an asset to any group. Taking the steps above and implementing the results will go a long way towards demonstrating to your volunteers the value your organisation places on them. It will also help you to feel confident your first aid needs are being met.

When you have completed this chapter, turn to the Checklist on page 105 and tick off the actions you have taken.

CHAPTER 11

Individuals with Specific Needs

Specific Needs

Certain individuals have needs which are specific and should be considered when developing policies and procedures for health and safety. Any risk assessment you carry out should be thorough in considering the needs of people who will or may be involved in your organisation's activities, but we have outlined some particular examples below.

PREGNANT WOMEN

The Management regulations (see chapter 5) were amended with effect from 1st December 1994 to implement the European Directive on Pregnant Workers. The Regulations now specifically require employers to take particular attention to risks that could affect the health and safety of expectant or new mothers, and their babies. Pregnant workers are especially at risk from manual handling activities, for example hormonal changes can affect the ligaments, increasing susceptibility to injury, and postural problems may increase as the pregnancy progresses. Other potential risks include long working hours, unrealistic targets and lack of control over the work, which may lead to stress.

CHILDREN AND YOUNG PERSONS

Any activity involving children has to be given special attention regarding safety. The Children's Act 1993 imposes duties on those who take on a caring role. Your local authority should be consulted regarding any child caring activity you take on.

Restrictions on the employment of children

For employment purposes the following definitions apply: a child is under the school leaving age of 16, and a young person is under the age of 18.

No children under 13 can be employed in any capacity*, and no child between 13 and 16 can be employed during school hours, before 7.00 am and after 7.00 pm on any day, for more than 2 hours on any school day, or for more than 2 hours on Sunday.

The work of 13 to 16 year olds can be controlled by local authority bye-laws so check before you enter into any employment situation.

Information given to parents about health risks

Before the employment of their child, parents or guardians must be given information on the assessed health and safety risks and the preventative and protective measures you propose to undertake.

* *Children and Young Persons Act 1993*

Young Persons

The Health and Safety (Young Persons) Regulations 1997 amend the Management of Health and Safety at Work Regulations 1992 to include risk assessments involving the employment of young persons, which must be carried out before they start work. You must take into account the following:

- inexperience, lack of awareness and immaturity of the young person
- layout of the workplace
- exposure to dangerous physical, chemical and biological agents
- the work equipment
- the processes and activities
- health and safety training
- specific agents and processes.*

MONITORING

Where the assessment shows that there is a risk to safety, physical or mental health or development of the young person, then monitoring of health must be provided on a regular basis.

Information for employees

Young people employed must be given comprehensive information on:

- the risks to health and safety identified by the risk assessment
- the preventive and the protective measures
- the emergency procedures to be adopted in dangerous situations
- the identity of those persons who have responsibility for implementing emergency procedures
- other risks that are present in the workplace caused by other employers sharing the workplace.

DISABLED STAFF

The disability Discrimination Act 1995 introduced new laws and measures aimed at ending the discrimination that many disabled people face in their day-to-day lives. The employment provision of the Act – Disability Discrimination (Employment) Regulations 1996 – came into force on 2nd December 1996, and is an attempt to protect people with disabilities, and those who have been disabled, from discrimination in the area of employment.

All employers with more than 20 staff will have to take measures to avoid discriminating against disabled persons and will have to make necessary changes in order to 'reasonably accommodate' such workers in their business.

** Refer to the Health and Safety (Young Persons) Regulations 1997*

Disabled people are a valuable and untapped resource in our society, and charities and voluntary organisations particularly have a duty to avoid treating them in a discriminatory manner.

Employers must make 'reasonable adjustments' if their employment arrangements or premises place disabled people at a substantial disadvantage compared to able bodied people.

What might be a 'reasonable adjustment'?

The Act makes it unlawful for an employer to discriminate against a disabled person for any reason which relates to their disability in respect of selection, recruitment, promotion, training or terms of employment, including benefits and working conditions.

If you don't recruit someone who uses a wheelchair because the workstation is inaccessible to wheelchairs, this is seen as less favourable treatment relating to the disability, rather than to the person's ability to do the job. You could not justify the treatment of the applicant if, for example, a simple reorganisation of furniture would ease access but you failed to do this, and you might lose if the case was brought to an industrial tribunal.

Example 1*

An employer shortlisting applicants for a junior office position is considering whether or not to interview a blind applicant whom the employer believes might present a safety risk moving around a crowded office space. A reasonable adjustment might be to provide mobility training to familiarise the new employee with the work area, so removing any risk.

The Act also outlaws discrimination by providers of goods and services, such as doctors, dentists, shops, libraries, restaurants and museums. If your organisation offers such services, you should already have considered how the Act may affect your work practices and work environment.

You can only treat a disabled person less favourably if you reasonably believe that either the disabled person or others may come to harm if you do not. Your reasons must always be genuine in these circumstances.

Example 2 †

A wheelchair user with a back injury wants to work out using weights at a local gym. The supervisor believes the customer to be at risk of injuring themselves. However if the disabled customer asserts, for example, that a doctor has advised that exercise will not strain their back, the supervisor must be prepared to change their decision.

This section can only briefly cover the Act, and you are advised to seek further information from:

- Disability on the Agenda, Freepost, London, SE99 7EQ, or tel: 0345 622 633, or textphone 0345 622 644.

---

* *example taken from The Disability Discrimination Act (What Employers Need to Know)*

† *example taken from The Disability Discrimination Act (What Service Providers Need to Know))*

CHAPTER 12

Food Hygiene

Food Safety

The supply of food and drinks is a common activity in the majority of voluntary organisations, for both refreshment to members and for fundraising. The requirement to provide food and drink which is safe is absolute, any person falling ill as a result of your culinary activities may be able to seek damages if you have been negligent. There is a general duty of care to provide wholesome, safe food and drink in all circumstances, but if you are providing food for sale, you have to comply with the regulations below.

Illness and deaths due to food poisoning have been given a high media profile in recent years. At the time of writing, a new food agency is proposed and you are recommended to check on any changes to the registration of premises which may result, from February 1998.

We have included the main requirements of the Food Safety Act 1990 as well as various Regulations. Throughout the regulations the word food includes drink for human consumption including alcoholic drinks.

The Food Safety Act 1990 requires that food for human consumption is safe and not falsely labelled or presented. There are other regulations regarding food hygiene made under this Act and the three component areas of which may apply to voluntary organisations are outlined below.

The Food Safety (General Food Hygiene) Regulations 1995

These create the basic framework for food hygiene law, specifying the basic hygiene conditions for food businesses. These regulations apply to food which is produced commercially for profit and food produced by voluntary groups or any other non-profit making organisation.

The persons in charge must ensure that:

- food handlers are supervised and trained in food hygiene matters;
- those in charge of the food production control the quality of the food by good management of hygiene.

The Regulations also require:

- personal hygiene for persons handling food
- sanitary provision and wash basins
- clean work area and equipment
- suitable premises
- arrangements for food waste
- arrangements for moveable or temporary premises, including transport – eg. check that the site is suitable, and the water supply must be wholesome and without risk.

The Food Safety (Temperature Control) Regulations 1995

These specify the temperature at which foods that are likely to support the growth of pathogenic bacteria must be kept. Generally speaking, food which can support bacterial growth must be kept at temperatures lower than 8°C or higher than 60°C – check the temperature gauges on fridges or hot plates.

The Food Premises (Registration) Regulations 1995

These require that food premises (including vehicles) be registered by the Local Authorities, in order that the premises can be inspected. Organisations dealing with food must register with the Local Authority (usually the EHSD), if their premises are used on five or more consecutive days or they are used on more than five days in any five consecutive weeks.

You will not be required to register if you supply beverages/biscuits to a business whose main activity is not the sale of food, or if you supply food via automatic vending machines. A maximum fine of £1,000 can be imposed for failing to register with the Local Authority so you are well advised to check.

The Food Safety Act 1990 and the Regulations allow a defence of due diligence. Here the defendant needs to show that they took all the reasonable precautions and records of systems of control, training records, cleaning regimes and risk assessments will need to be evident.

If catering is a regular activity there will be a need for key personnel who handle food (including volunteers) to attend a basic Food & Hygiene Certificate Course. For details of such a course in your area, contact the local EHSD.

When you have completed this chapter, turn to the Checklist on page 105 and tick off the actions you have taken.

CHAPTER 13

Recording & Reporting of Sickness, Incidents & Accidents

Recording Incidents

The recording of your accidents and incidents is an essential part of any health and safety procedure, even if there is no injury, and however many employees or volunteers you may have. By investigating and recording all accidents and incidents, you can identify action to prevent further accidents. It is also a good idea to record and investigate all 'near misses' – today's near miss could be tomorrow's accident.

By law:

- All workplaces with more than 10 employees, and all factories, must have an accident book where details of all accidents can be recorded.
- They should also be used to record any sickness possibly caused or made worse by work, and dangerous occurrences or 'near-misses' in the workplace.
- The book should be kept for at least 3 years after the last entry.

An example of a form suitable for use in investigating accidents and incidents is provided at the end of the chapter. The form in your policy can be used as your accident and incident book.

The Reporting of Injuries, Diseases and Dangerous Occurrences Regulations 1995 (RIDDOR)

These require that all work-related accidents, diseases and dangerous occurrences are reported to the appropriate enforcing authority. This is a legal requirement for employers, the self-employed and those in control of work premises. Note that any injury which results in a member of the public being taken to hospital is also reportable.

You must report the following to the HSE or the EHSD, depending on who has registered your business:

- ***Death or major injury (including as a result of physical assault).*** Such an event should be reported forthwith to the relevant enforcing authority by the quickest practicable means i.e. telephone or fax using an approved form (F2508) – available from The Stationery Office (telephone number in your local directory) – and confirmed in writing within ten working days.
- ***Over-three-day injury.*** If there is an accident connected with work (including an act of physical violence), and your employee, or a self-employed person working on your premises suffers an over-three-day absence due to an injury, you must send a completed accident report form (F2508) to the enforcing authority within ten days. An over-three-day injury is one which is not a major injury but results in the injured person being away from work or unable to do their normal work for more than three days (including non-working days).
- ***Disease.*** If a doctor notifies you that your employee suffers from a reportable work-related disease, then you must complete the disease report form (F2508A) to the relevant enforcing authority .

- ***Dangerous occurrences***. If something happens which does not result in a reportable injury, but which clearly could have done, then it may be a dangerous occurrence, such as a fire or explosion caused by electrical short circuit, or the accidental release of a substance into the atmosphere which may damage health, which did not injure anyone but clearly could have. This must be reported immediately to the enforcing authority using form F2508.

Volunteers only

For all organisations, it is good practice to record any accidents, incidents or near misses in order to identify any action which would help to prevent a similar event occurring.

Organisations with volunteers only, and who do not own premises, are not bound by the RIDDOR regulations, but they are required to inform their insurance company of any incident or accident, and obviously any major injury or death must be reported to the emergency authorities.

When you have completed this chapter, turn to the Checklist on page 105 and tick off the actions you have taken.

EXAMPLE OF AN ACCIDENT FORM

General details of incident

- Date of incident ....
- Exact location of incident ....
- Is the organisation in overall control of the premises/event? ☐ Yes ☐ No
- If no, give the name of the owner/leaseholder ....

Type of incident

☐ fatality
☐ over 3 day injury
☐ under 3 day injury
☐ physical assault
☐ specified major injury
☐ dangerous occurrence
☐ damage incident

Injured person

- Full name ....
- Age .... Sex **M/F**
- Address ....
- Nature of injury (state left or right as appropriate) ....
- Status of injured person (tick as appropriate)

☐ employee of organisation
☐ volunteer (includes members of governing body)
☐ employee of another organisation
☐ person being cared for by organisation
☐ self-employed person
☐ contractor
☐ member of general public

- Role in organisation ....
- How long with organisation?..............................yrs ....mths
- What was injured person doing at time of incident? ....
- Was this something they were authorised to do? ☐ Yes ☐ No
- Were they authorised to be where the incident occurred? ☐ Yes ☐ No
- When was the incident reported to you?...................................date .... time
- Was the incident witnessed by someone else? ☐ Yes ☐ No
- Was first aid treatment given on site? ☐ Yes ☐ No Details ....
- Was hospital/medical treatment obtained? ☐ Yes ☐ No Details ....
- Anticipate absence from organisation: ☐ no time lost ☐ less than 3 days ☐ 3 days or more?

Further details of accident ....

List training requirements to prevent reoccurrence: ....

Signed by: .... Date ....

Name ....

EXAMPLE OF AN ACCIDENT FORM

General data [illegible]

• Date [illegible]

• Exact location of accident [illegible]

• [illegible] under the control of the premises [illegible] ☐ Yes ☐ No

If no, give the name of [illegible]

Type of incident

☐ fatal ☐ specified major injury

☐ over 3 day injury ☐ dangerous occurrence

☐ under 3 day injury ☐ [illegible]

☐ physical assault

Injured person

• Full name

• Age [illegible] Sex M/F

• Address

• Nature of injury (state if [illegible] applicable)

• Status of injured person (tick as appropriate)

☐ employee of organisation ☐ self-employed person

☐ volunteer working on behalf of governing body ☐ contractor

☐ employee of another organisation ☐ member of general public

☐ person in care cared for by organisation

• Role in organisation

• How long with organisation? [illegible] months

• What was injured person doing at time of incident? [illegible]

• Was this something they were authorised to do? ☐ Yes ☐ No

• Were they authorised to be where the incident occurred? ☐ Yes ☐ No

• When was the incident reported to you? [illegible] Date [illegible] Time

• Was the incident witnessed by someone else? ☐ Yes ☐ No

• Was first aid treatment given on site? ☐ Yes ☐ No Details [illegible]

• Was hospital/medical treatment obtained? ☐ Yes ☐ No Details [illegible]

• Anticipate absence from work/volunteering ☐ none ☐ less than 3 days ☐ 3 days or more

Further details of accident

• List training requirements to prevent recurrence

Completed by [illegible] Date [illegible]

[illegible]

CHAPTER 14

Information, Training & Instruction

Safety Representatives and Safety Committees

Regulations require that employers consult with employees on health and safety matters. The Health & Safety (Consultation with Employees) Regulations 1996 apply to all employees, and the Safety Representatives and Safety Committees Regulations 1977 are applicable to employees who are members of recognised trade unions.

There is evidence from the TUC that where information is made readily available to people and they are party to the decision making process regarding the way activities are developed and carried out, the number of accidents occurring is reduced.

We recommend that:

- larger voluntary groups should adopt the procedure of establishing a Safety Committee to oversee health and safety within their organisation;
- discussions on matters of health and safety information should be a regular agenda item for your management committee meetings, and any decisions should be minuted and made available to all members.

Generally speaking, the more information on matters of health and safety that are made available to people, the better informed and equipped they are to avoid accidents and make decisions regarding their health and safety.

By law* employers must display copies of the following:

- a current certificate from your insurance company showing that you have employers' liability insurance;
- The Health & Safety Law poster for employees†. Alternatively give a leaflet to each individual;
- action to be taken in the case of fire, how to raise the alarm, what to do when the alarm is sounded, how to call the fire brigade, fire escape route, muster points, emergency exits, fire extinguisher points, fire doors (as designated on the fire certificate);
- location of first aid point/box, name and location of trained first aid persons or the appointed person;
- copy of any specific information or posters regarding regulations that apply to your premises where it is a requirement of those regulations to display information, eg. the Abrasive Wheels Regulations 1970, the Woodworking Regulations 1974.

There is also a legal requirement to give people access to copies of the health and safety policy.

---

* *Employers' Liability (Compulsory Insurance) Act 1969*

† *Poster 'Health and Safety – What you should know' ISBN 011 7014294*

INFORMATION AND TRAINING

Following assessments, all staff and volunteers must have information and training on the following, as required:

- emergency evacuation procedures (including fire)
- accident reporting
- first aid treatment and facilities
- arrangements for the health and safety problems specifically relating to their work. These will include: rules and regulations and risk assessments of their workplace.

When you have completed this chapter, turn to the Checklist on page 105 and tick off the actions you have taken.

APPENDIX 1

Checklist

Progress Checklist				
Chapter	**Have you:**	**YES**	**Not applicable**	**You should enter these into the relevant part of your Health & Safety Policy** (see pp 109-115)
2 **Your health & safety policy**	• prepared your health & safety policy statement of intent?			**In Part 1 (Policy)** Statement of Intent
3 **Registering your activity**	• notified the relevant agency? • applied for any appropriate licence?			**In Part 2 (Organisation)** Name the person who has made the application **In Part 3 (Arrangements)** Include details of conditions of the registration/licence
4 **Insurance**	• insured against identified risks?			**In Part 2** Name of person in organisation responsible for insurance **In Part 3** Details of the insurance cover obtained
5 **Health, safety and welfare**	• identified those Acts and Regulations which could apply to your organisation?			**In Part 2** Names of those persons attending to each specific piece of legislation **In Part 3** List applicable Acts/Regulations and proposed ways of achieving compliance
6 **Risk assessment**	• prepared a list of risks which need assessment and introduced a plan to carry them out?			**In Part 3** The risk assessments and details of the procedures to be followed to eliminate or reduce the risk
7 **COSHH assessments**	• identified substances present which are hazardous?			**In Part 3** The COSHH assessments and procedures required to control the use of the substances
8 **Fire**	• applied for fire certificate? • completed fire records and information form? • carried out fire risk assessments? • devised fire and emergency procedures including training?			**In Part 3** Details of the restrictions requirements of the fire certificate **In Part 2** The person responsible for ensuring equipment is serviced **In Part 3** Assessments and procedures required to control the risks **In Part 2** Those persons with responsibilities in the procedures **In Part 3** Details of the fire procedures

Progress Checklist

Chapter	Have you:	YES	Not applicable	You should enter these into the relevant part of your Health & Safety Policy (see pp 109-115)
9 **Violence**	• identified the risks associated with violence and carried out risk assessments?			**In Part 3** Assessments and procedures required to control the risks
10 **Young persons**	• considered the responsibilities regarding children and young people? • carried out risk assessments			**In Part 2** Those persons with responsibilities for children and young persons **In Part 3** Assessments and procedures required to control the risks
11 **First aid**	• carried out risk assessment to decide first aid requirements?			**In Part 2** Those persons with responsibilities for first aid **In Part 3** Assessment and procedures required to meet the first aid requirements including training and information
12 **Food hygiene**	• determined how the legislation relating to food affects your organisation?			**In Part 2** The person responsible for registering food activities to the EHSD **In Part 3** Procedures required to meet the food hygiene requirements including training and information
13 **Recording and reporting of sickness, incidents and accidents**	• established your accident reporting and investigation procedure?			**In Part 2** Those persons with responsibilities for accident reporting and investigation **In Part 3** Systems and procedures required to record and investigate accidents including training and knowledge of the procedures
14 **Information, training and instruction**	• identified the information and training required? • implemented measures to meet those needs?			**In Part 2** Those persons with responsibilities for training and instruction **In Part 3** Training and information which has to be given

APPENDIX 2

Blank Health & Safety Policy

Health and Safety Policy

Part 1: General Statement of Policy

Part 1

This document is the health and safety policy of (name of organisation):

....

Our policy is to provide healthy and safe working conditions, equipment and systems of work for all our employees, volunteers and members, and to provide all such training and information as is necessary. We also accept responsibility for all other people who may be affected by our activities.

This policy will be kept up to date, particularly as the organisation changes in nature and size. It will be reviewed at least once a year.

Overall and final reponsibility is vested in:

Name: ....

Position: ....

Date: ....

Note: *the person named above should be a senior person in your organisation.*

Even if the responsibility is delegated to one person, the actual responsibility is shared between all members of the governing body.

Health and Safety Policy Part 2: Organisation of health and safety

Person with overall responsibility

The person with overall responsibility for health and safety in this organisation is:

....

Registration of the activity (fill in a) or b) as appropriate)

a) The activity was registered with ....on (date): ....

and form ....was completed and sent.

Signed: .... Date:....................................

b) Having contacted ....on ....
I was informed there is no need to register the activity.

Signed: .... Date:....................................

If you change your activities, fill in section c)

c) The owner/leaseholder of the property was notified of our activity on..................................

Signed: .... Date:....................................

Fire precautions

The person with overall responsibility for fire precautions is: ....

If the following tasks are delegated, fill in names of people given responsibility **Date**

a) Initial risk assessment and contact with Fire Brigade: ....

b) Obtaining and organising the maintenance and testing of fire equipment and keeping records: ....

c) Completing the fire drill procedure:.. ....

d) Compiling the fire notices: ....

e) Preparing the emergency evacuation procedure: ....

f) Responsible for the fire register: ....

g) Making sure drill is carried out on regular basis: ....

Insurance

The person responsible for insuring the activity of the organisation is:

First aid

a) The person responsible for first aid assessment in the organisation: ....

b) The first aider(s) in the organisation is/are: ....

....

Recording and reporting of accidents and incidents

The person responsible for investigating, recording and reporting accidents and incidents

(including violence) is: ....

Health and Safety Policy Part 3: Arrangements and procedures

General fire safety

a) Local Fire Brigade contact name: .... Tel no:.............................

b) Company hired to check, maintain and service fire safety equipment:

Company name: ....

Address: ....

....

....

....

Contact name: .... Tel no:.................................

c) List of equipment and its location:

Item	Location	Service date

d) Fire certificate issued by: .... **Renewal date:**. ....

e) Notes ....

....

....

....

....

....

Health and Safety Policy Part 3(cont): Arrangements and procedures

f) Notice of procedure in case of fire

If you discover a fire:

1 Operate the fire alarm without putting yourself in danger

2 Go to your place of assembly at:..

3 Call the Fire Brigade on 999

On hearing the fire alarm:

1 Leave the building by the quickest available route

2 Go to your place of assembly at:..

Do not leave the assembly point until told to do so by: ....

Do not return to the building until told to do so by: ....

g) Location of fire exits, extinguishers, escape routes, assembly points (with a map of the premises)

Note: *All notices must comply with the Safety Sign Regulations e.g. "Must do" signs should be in blue and of a certain size.*

Health and Safety Policy Part 3(cont): Arrangements and procedures

Employer's liability insurance form

Name of insurance company: ....

Address: ....

....

....

Telephone number:.. Contact:..

Policy number:..

Date of expiry:..

Amount insured: ....

Special exclusions: ....

Special conditions:..

Public liability insurance form

Name of insurance company: ....

Address: ....

....

....

Telephone number:.. Contact:..

Policy number:..

Date of expiry:..

Amount insured: ....

Special exclusions: ....

Special conditions:..

Health and Safety Policy Part 3(cont): Arrangements and procedures

Special risk insurance:

The following items and risks will be insured:

....

....

....

....

Driver Registration Form

Organisation's name: ....

Address: ....

....

....

Driver's name: .... Age:................ yrs................ mths

Address: ....

....

....

Driving licence number: ....

Licence checked? ☐ Yes ☐ No Date checked: ....Date passed test:........................

Endorsement points:..............Completed minibus test? ☐ Yes ☐ No Date:..............................

Approved to drive vehicles only ....

Medical conditions: ....

Checked:

☐ medical certificate ☐ appropriate insurance cover

☐ occasional cover insurance ☐ insurance document enclosed?

Declaration:

The above details are, to the best of my knowledge, complete and accurate.

Signed (employee) .... Date:.........................

Signed (on behalf of organisation) .... Date:.........................

Health and Safety Policy Part 3(cont): Arrangements and procedures

List the Acts and Regulations which are applicable to your organisation:

....

....

....

....

....

....

....

....

....

Risk Assessment

The following assessments have been carried out:

	Yes	N/A	Date
Health and safety			
COSHH			
Fire			
Violence			
First aid			
Young persons			

APPENDIX 3

Points of Contact for the HSE

Points of contact for the Health and Safety Executive (HSE)

The way of contacting the HSE will depend on where you work or the information you want.

All general enquiries and information

There is a national telephone public enquiry service called HSE Infoline 0541 545500, open 8.30am - 5.00pm, Monday to Friday.

Regional Information Centres

These are for personal callers who want to consult information held at these centres, and they are open 9.00am to 5.00pm, Monday to Friday.

London Information Centre:
Rose Court, 2 Southwark Bridge, London SE1 9HS

Bootle Information Centre
HSE, Information Centre, St Hugh's House, Stanley Precinct, Bootle, Merseyside L20 3QY

Sheffield Information Centre:
(for written or faxed enquiries, as well as personal callers)

HSE, Information Centre, Broad Lane, Sheffield, S3 7HQ (Fax: 0114 289 2333)

HSE Publications

Free leaflets and priced publications can be ordered from HSE Books directly:

HSE Books, P.O. Box 1999, Sudbury, Suffolk, CO10 6FS (Tel: 01787 881165; Fax 01787 313995)

HSE Regional Offices

Head Office	2 Southwark Bridge, London, SE1 9HS 0171 717 6000
South West	Inter City House, Mitchell Lane, Victoria Street, Bristol, BS1 6AN 0117 886000
South	Priestly House, Priestly Road, Basingstoke, RG24 9NW 01256 404000
South East	3 East Grinstead House, London Road, East Grinstead, West Sussex, RH19 1RR 01342 334200
London North	Maritime House, 1 Unton Road, Barking, Essex, IG11 8HF 0181 235 8000
London South	1 Long Lane, London, SE1 4PG 0171 516 2100
East Anglia	39 Baddow Road, Chelmsford, Essex, CM2 0HL 01245 706200
Home Counties North	14 Cardiff Road, Luton, Beds, LU1 1PP 01582 444200
East Midlands	5th Floor, Belgrave House, 1 Greyfriars, Northampton, NN1 2BS 01604 738300
West Midlands	McLaren Building, 2 Masshouse Circus, Queensway, Birmingham, B4 7NP 0121 607 6200
Wales	Brunel House, 2 Fitzalan Road, Cardiff, CF2 1SH 01222 263000
West Region	The Marches House, Midway, Newcastle-under-Lyme, Staffs, ST5 1DT 01782 602300
North Midlands	The Pearson Building, 55 Upper Parliament Street, Nottingham, NG1 6AU 01159 712800
S. Yorkshire	Sovereign House, 110 Queen Street, Sheffield, S1 2ES 0114 291 2300
W. and N. Yorkshire	8 St Pauls Street, Leeds, LS1 2LE 0113 283 4200
Greater Manchester	Quay House, Quay Street, Manchester, M3 8JB 0161 952 8200
North West	Victoria House, Ormskirk Road, Preston, PR1 1HH 01772 836200
	The Triad, Stanley Road, Bootle, Merseyside, L20 3PG 0151 479 2200
North East	Arden House, Regent Centre, Gosforth, Newcastle-upon-Tyne, NE3 3JN 0191 202 6200
Scotland East	Belford House, 59 Belford Road, Edinburgh, EH4 3UE 0131 247 2000
Scotland West	375 West George Street, Glasgow, G2 4LW 0141 275 3000

APPENDIX 4

Legislation

Legislation

Statutes

Children Act 1989.

Children and Young Persons Act 1933.

Disability Discrimination Act 1995.

Factories Act 1961.

Fire Precautions Act 1971.

Food Safety Act 1990.

Health and Safety at Work etc. Act 1974.

Occupiers Liability Acts 1957 and 1984.

Offices, Shops and Railway Premises Act 1963.

Regulations

Chemicals (Hazard Information and Packaging for Supply) Regulations 1994 (CHIP 2).

Constructions (Design and Management) Regulations 1994.

Control of Substances Hazardous to Health Regulations 1994 (COSHH).

Electricity at Work Regulations 1989.

Employers' Liability (Compulsory Insurance) Regulations General (Amendment) Regulations 1994.

Fire Precautions (Workplace) Regulations 1997.

Food Premises (Registration) Regulations 1991.

Food Safety (General Food Hygiene) Regulations 1995.

Food Safety (Temperature Control) Regulations 1995.

Gas Safety (Installation and Use) Regulations 1994.

Health and Safety (Consultation with Employees) Regulations 1996.

Health and Safety (Display Screen Equipment) Regulations 1992.

Health and Safety (First Aid) Regulations 1981.

Health and Safety (Safety Signs and Signals) Regulations 1996.

Health and Safety (Training for Work) Regulations 1990.

Health and Safety (Young Persons) Regulations 1997.

Highly Flammable Liquids and Petroleum Gases Regulations 1972.

Management of Health and Safety at Work Regulations 1992.

Manual Handling Operations Regulations 1992.

Noise at Work Regulations 1989.

Personnel Protection Equipment at Work Regulations 1992.

Provision & Uses of Work Equipment Regulations 1992.

Reporting of Injuries, Diseases & Dangerous Occurrences Regulations 1995 (RIDDOR).

Safety Representatives and Safety Committee Regulations 1977.

Workplace Health, Safety and Welfare Regulations 1992.